14·50

Project Director: J. J. Thompson, CBE

ASTROPHYSICS

NIGEL INGHAM

D0317937

Nelson

Thomas Nelson and Sons Ltd
Nelson House   Mayfield Road
Walton-on-Thames   Surrey
KT12 5PL   UK

ISBN 0-17-448239-6
NPN 9 8 7 6 5 4 3

Typeset by Florence Production Ltd, Stoodleigh, Devon
Printed in China

Contents

iv

The Project: an introduction

The **University of Bath Science 16–19 Project** grew out of a reappraisal of how far sixth form science had travelled during a period of unprecedented curriculum reform and from an attempt to evaluate future development. Changes were occurring both within the constitution of 16–19 syllabuses themselves and as a result of external pressures from 16+ and from below: syllabus redefinition (starting with the common cores), the introduction of AS-level and its academic recognition, the originally optimistic outcome to the Higginson enquiry, new emphasis on skills and processes, and the balance of continuous and final assessment at GCSE level.

This activity offered fertile ground for the School of Education at the University of Bath to join forces with a team of science teachers drawn from a wide spectrum of educational experience, and with a major publisher to create a flexible curriculum model and then develop resources to fit it. This group addressed the task of satisfying these requirements:

- the new syllabus and examination demands of A- and AS-level courses;
- the provision of materials suitable for both the core and option parts of syllabuses;
- the striking of an appropriate balance of opportunities for students to acquire knowledge and understanding, develop skills and concepts, and to appreciate the applications and implications of science;
- the encouragement of a degree of independent learning through highly interactive texts;
- the satisfaction of the needs of a wide ability range of students at this level.

Some of these objectives were easier to achieve than others. Relationships to still evolving syllabuses demand the most rigorous analysis and a sense of vision – and optimism – regarding their eventual destination. Original assumptions about AS-level, for example, as a distinct though complementary sibling to A-level needed to be revised.

The Project, though, always regarded itself as more than a provider of materials, important as this is, and concerned itself equally with the process of provision – how material can best be written and shaped to meet the requirements of the educational market-place. This aim found expression in two principal forms: the idea of secondment at the University and the extensive trialling of early material in schools and colleges.

Most authors enjoyed a period of secondment from teaching, which not only allowed them to reflect and write more strategically (and, particularly so, in a supportive academic environment) but, equally, to engage with each other in wrestling with the issues in question.

The Project saw in the trialling a crucial test for the acceptance of its ideas and their execution. Over one hundred institutions and one thousand students participated, and responses were invited from teachers and students alike. The reactions generally confirmed the soundness of the model and allowed for more scrupulous textual housekeeping, as details of confusion, ambiguity or plain misunderstanding were revised and reordered.

The test of all teaching must be in the quality of the learning, and the proof of these resources will be in the understanding and ease of accessibility which they generate. The Project, ultimately, is both a collection of materials and a message of faith in the science curriculum of the future.

J.J. Thompson

How to use this book

Interest in astronomy has grown substantially over recent years, with such events as the launch of the Hubble Space Telescope into Earth orbit, and the tentative identification of the first black holes. In addition to the fantastic photographs from the Hubble telescope, there are also pictures from the Voyager missions to the outer planets. These images conjure up questions: 'What are we seeing?' 'How did it happen?' 'Will people ever go there?'

Astrophysics and cosmology encompass everything from the smallest subatomic particles to the vast and expanding Universe. They deal with the remote past and make predictions about the distant future. The principal aim of this book is to provide a text that can accompany the modules on astronomy, astrophysics and cosmology offered by the various A-level examination boards. In addition, many teachers and pupils will have developed an interest in these areas during their work at GCSE level, and this book aims to extend this study for those who have a broad interest in everything to do with space.

Like other books in the University of Bath Science 16–19 series, we have assumed that the reader has someone to guide their learning, and who can help them to understand the more difficult aspects of the subject. Questions, assignments and investigations are provided to enable the reader to develop the ideas met in the text. Some of the calculations are quite tricky, and many require the use of a scientific calculator. Nevertheless, calculations can help to build a greater appreciation of some of the less familiar concepts, such as time dilation in Einstein's theory of relativity.

Finally, the sequence of concepts in the book is intended to provide a coherent development of the ideas, rather than to reflect the syllabus of any particular examination board. This should help anyone who has an interest in the subject and who wishes to gain a coherent picture of the Universe as a whole. If you are following an A-level course, I would recommend that you have a copy of the current syllabus to hand, so that you will be aware of the chapters that you will be tested on. I hope that you will wish to read the rest of the book so as to learn more about this fascinating subject. Without the Big Bang and the fusion processes that take place in the stars, neither you nor I would be here!

Learning objectives and Summaries

Learning objectives are given at the beginning of each chapter, and they outline what you should gain from that chapter. They are statements of attainment and often link closely to statements in a course syllabus. Learning objectives can help you to make notes for revision, especially if used in conjunction with the summaries at the ends of the chapters, as well as being useful for checking progress.

Questions

Some in-text questions occur at points when you should consolidate what you have just learned. Others will help you to prepare for what is to follow by thinking along the lines required by the question. Some questions can, therefore, be answered from the material covered in the previous section, whereas others may require additional thought or information. Answers to numerical (parts of) questions are given at the end of the book. Note that some are given to a greater degree of precision than is warranted by the question; this is to enable you to check that your working has been correct.

Investigations

Opportunities for practical work in astrophysics are limited. However, where appropriate, details have been included at relevant points in the text.

Assignments

Where you are asked to think about a particular idea, or to develop an idea further, you will find text and questions presented together as an assignment. You may need to refer to other sources of information; suitable resources are listed in Appendix C.

Mathematical derivations

There are some mathematical relationships that you may have to understand, and may also have to be able to derive. These derivations appear in Appendix B, so that they do not disrupt the flow of ideas in the text.

Other resources

You should find most of the information you require in your study of astrophysics within the pages of this book. However, astrophysics is a constantly developing subject, with new discoveries and new theories coming along all the time. You should look out for articles in this field in periodicals such as *New Scientist* and *Scientific American*, as well as popular astronomy magazines and the science pages of newspapers and other magazines. In Appendix C, you will find a list of some suggested sources.

Acknowledgements

The author would like to thank: David Sang, for his advice, encouragement and practical help; and Liz Swinbank (University of York), for her expertise in ensuring the accuracy of the subject matter. The author would also like to thank John Turl for his contributions and expertise in improving the accuracy of the text at reprint.

The author and publishers wish to thank the following, who have kindly given permission to reproduce copyright material:

> The University of Cambridge Local Examinations Syndicate, the Northern Examinations and Assessment Board, and Edexcel Foundation, London Examinations (ULEAC), for questions from their past examination papers; New Science Publications for material by Nigel Henbest from *New Scientist* magazine, 6 March 1986.

The author and publishers wish to acknowledge, with thanks, the following photographic sources:

> Ann Ronan for *Figure 1.3, p 3; Figure 1.9, p 6; Figure 1.10, p 7; Figures 1.11 and 1.12, p 8; Figures 1.13 and 1.14, p 9; Figure 1.17, p 11; Figure 1.20, p 13; Figure 2.1, p 15; Figure 2.2, p 16.* ARP for *Figure 4.3a, b and c, p 42.* Exley Publications for *Figure 1.2, p 3.* Galaxy Picture Library for *Figure 6.13, p 85; Figure 9.9, p 123; Figure 9.16, p 126; Figure 10.1, p 128.* Image Select Int. Ltd for *Theme 2, p 39; Figure 5.21, p 69; Figure 7.17, p 98; Theme 3a, p 105; Figure 8.2, p 108; Figure 9.6, p 122; Figure 9.11, p 123; Figure 9.13, p 125; Figure 10.3, p 130; Figure 11.3, p 142.* New Scientist for *Figure 4.7, p 46.* Robert Scotts Associates for *Figure 4.1, p 41.* Science Photo Library for *Theme 1, p 1; Figure 3.6, p 25; Figure 4.6, p 46; Figure 4.10, p 48; Figure 4.14a and b, p 51; Figure 4.17a and b, p 52; Figure 4.19a and b, p 53; Figure 5.10, p 62; Figures 5.11, 5.12a and b, p 63; Figure 5.19, p 67; Figure 5.22, p 69; Figure 5.23, p 70; Figure 5.24a, b, c and d, p 71; Figure 6.1, p 75; Figure 6.4, p 79; Figure 6.8, p 81; Figure 7.7, p 91; Figure 7.12, p 94; Theme 3b, p 105; Figure 8.7, p 114; Figure 9.5, p 121; Figure 9.7, p 123; Figure 9.14, p 126; Figure 10.5, p 131; Figure 10.7a and b, p 133; Figure 10.10, p 134; Figures 10.12 and 10.13, p 136; Figure 10.17, p 138; Figure 11.5, p 145; Figure 11.6, p 146.* The author for *Figure 6.6, p 80.* Tony Stone for *Figure 11.1, p 141.*

Every effort has been made to trace all the copyright holders, but if any have been inadvertently overlooked the publishers will be pleased to make the necessary arrangement at the first opportunity.

Theme **1**

PEOPLE AND IDEAS

Astronomy is one of the oldest areas of study, whether as part of astrology, where the ancients strove to predict the future, or more scientifically in knowing when to sow crops, or as a navigational aid. It is thought that the stone circle at Stonehenge formed part of an ancient observatory.

The first three chapters of this book look at the people who have shaped our knowledge of the Universe, from the ancient Egyptians to the 20th-century ideas of Albert Einstein. These are the people whose ideas have helped us to develop our modern understanding of the Universe.

Stonehenge, in Wiltshire, is thought by some astronomers to have been an early form of observatory. Its stones are aligned on significant points in the sky, like here at the midsummer sunrise.

Modern observatories, such as the European Southern Observatory in Chile shown here, are often situated on mountain summits, where they can avoid most of the distorting effects of the Earth's atmosphere.

Chapter 1

THE ORIGINS OF ASTRONOMY AND COSMOLOGY

There is ample evidence that ancient peoples were interested in astronomy. They made observations of the movements of the stars and planets, and developed theories of the nature of the Universe. This chapter, which is the least mathematical part of the book, provides a concise outline of some of the ideas that existed prior to the work of Isaac Newton, the first scientist to apply rigorous mathematical methods to the study of astronomy.

LEARNING OBJECTIVES

After studying this chapter you should be able to:

1. understand the observations that led to the ancient models of the Universe;

2. describe the progress in the understanding of the Universe that resulted from the work of Copernicus, Kepler and Galileo.

1.1 EARLY ASTRONOMY

Fig 1.1 Stonehenge, an ancient astronomical device.

The ancients

Stonehenge (Fig 1.1) is a familiar part of the landscape of southern England. It is believed that these prehistoric stones are part of an astronomical device. Parts of Stonehenge date back to around 2800 BC, although the massive stones are more recent, dating back to the structure's completion around 2000 BC. Initially, Stonehenge consisted of a circular ditch with a diameter of about 80 m, inside which there was a concentric bank, and a long Avenue leading to the north-east. Outside this structure, the Heelstone stands in the Avenue.

The significance of the Heelstone was realised by W. Stukely in 1740, when he suggested that the Avenue pointed towards the point at which the Sun rises at the summer solstice (in June, when the Sun reaches its most northerly position in the sky). As seen from the centre of the circle, this is directly over the Heelstone. Since then, it has been suggested that other sight lines point to the most northerly and southerly risings of the Moon. (The direction in which the Moon rises varies slightly over the course of a year.) All of this is, however, speculative, since no written records exist from the time when Stonehenge was in use.

Similarly, early astronomy flourished in Central and South America, where many temples were built by the Mayan and Aztec empires. These often aligned with the solstice rising of the Sun and other significant positions, such as the extreme points at which the planet Venus rose and set. An example of such an observatory is shown in Fig 1.2.

Fig 1.2 This observatory in Mexico was built to allow ancient Mayan peoples to make astronomical predictions.

Archaeo-astronomy, the study of the astronomy of ancient peoples, reveals the fact that these people were enquiring and observed the night sky. However, owing to the lack of written manuscripts, we can only speculate about what they thought. Our present understanding of the Universe begins with the Greek civilisation, mainly due to the fact that some of their manuscripts survived, so that others could build on their ideas.

Greek astronomy

Greek astronomy built upon the observations and ideas of the Babylonian and Egyptian cultures, which were influenced by religion and astrology. Plato (428 BC–347 BC), although not an astronomer, was one of the first to suggest the concept of the perfection of circular motion for the motion of the planets. This idea was developed by his student, Eudoxus of Cnidus (409 BC–356 BC), who suggested that the planets are attached to concentric crystal spheres, with the Earth at their centre. This model could not explain the varying brightness of the planets as they move across the night sky; nevertheless, the idea of perfectly circular orbits was to last nearly two thousand years, until Kepler proposed that the planets moved in ellipses.

Aristotle (384 BC–322 BC) was one of the most eminent thinkers of the ancient Greek civilisation. As he gathered many of the ideas together, he became the authority on the structure of the Universe. He developed a **geocentric** model, with the corrupt and changeable Earth at its centre, and the Heavens, which were perfect, above. To account for the movement of celestial objects across the sky, the spheres whirled westwards. The whole Universe was not thought to be much bigger than the Earth – see Fig 1.3.

Ironically, less than a century after Aristotle, the Alexandrian astronomer Aristarchus of Samos proposed a model in which the Earth rotated on its

Fig 1.3 In Aristotle's model of the Universe, the Earth is stationary at the centre. It is orbited by the Moon (*Lunæ*), and then the other planets, together with the Sun (*Solis*). This woodcut dates from 1537, long after Aristotle's time.

THE ORIGINS OF ASTRONOMY AND COSMOLOGY

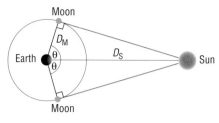

FIRST QUARTER

THIRD QUARTER

Fig 1.4 Aristarchus's method for calculating the relative distances of the Moon and the Sun from the Earth. Using trigonometry, $\cos \theta = D_M/D_S = 1/20$.

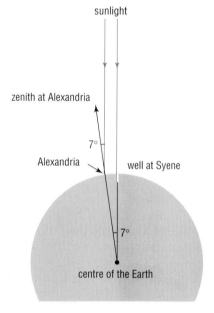

Fig 1.5 Eratosthenes' experiment to find the Earth's circumference.

axis, whilst travelling around the Sun. Unfortunately, such was the regard for Aristotle that this model did not gain a great deal of support. Later, many of Aristarchus's writings were lost, and so the idea of a Sun-centred (**heliocentric**) Universe was to disappear until Copernicus, almost two thousand years later.

One of Aristarchus's achievements was to devise a method of determining the relative distances to the Sun and Moon. He knew that, at the times of the Moon's first and third quarters, the Earth–Moon–Sun angle must be 90°, as shown in Fig 1.4. By applying geometry based on observations of the time, he deduced that the Sun must be at least 20 times further away than the Moon (the currently accepted value is 390 times as far).

Aristarchus then made an attempt to reason out the comparative sizes of the Earth, Moon and Sun using lunar eclipses, when the Moon passes into the Earth's shadow. From the size of the shadow that was formed on the Moon, he deduced that the Earth was clearly bigger than the Moon. Aristarchus pointed out that the Moon and Sun have the same angular diameters, and their distances must be in the same proportion as their diameters. Hence, according to him, the Sun must have a diameter 20 times that of the Moon.

It is often said that the ancients believed the Earth was flat. However, the perfection of spheres had led Aristotle to conclude that the Earth was spherical, particularly as it always cast a round shadow during lunar eclipses. He did, however, have a limited idea of the Earth's size. Around 200 BC, Eratosthenes of Alexandria found a way to calculate the Earth's radius. Working in the Library, he read that, in the city of Syene (Aswan) in southern Egypt, there was a well down which the sunlight shone vertically on the day of the summer solstice. But on the same day in Alexandria (in northern Egypt), the Sun was about 1/50th of the circumference of the sky (about 7°) south of the zenith – see Fig 1.5.

Using simple geometry, Eratosthenes inferred that the distance from Alexandria to Syene was 1/50th of the Earth's circumference. From an estimate of this distance, he was able to work out values for the circumference and radius of the Earth. His results were not very different from today's accepted values.

ASSIGNMENT

The following information will help you to reproduce Eratosthenes' calculations (distances are given in an ancient unit, the stadium):

> time taken to travel from Alexandria to Syene
>   (on a camel) = 50 days
> distance travelled by a camel in 1 day = 100 stadia
> 6 stadia = 1 kilometre (approximately)

1.1 Use Eratosthenes' data to deduce the circumference and the radius of the Earth.

1.2 The currently accepted value for the Earth's average radius is 6378 km. Show that Eratosthenes' value was within 4% of this.

The Ptolemaic model

One of the greatest of the ancient astronomers was Hipparchos, who lived around 150 BC. As well as being credited with the invention of trigonometry, he compiled the first star catalogue, and discovered the **precession**

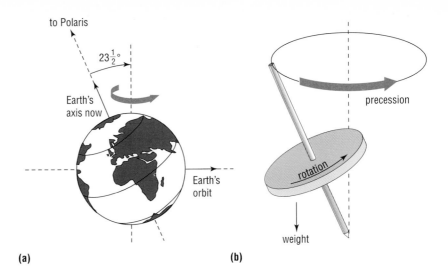

Fig 1.6 The Earth's axis precesses slowly, in much the same way as the axis of a spinning top moves.

(a)   **(b)**

of the celestial pole. This is the slow change in the direction of the Earth's axis of rotation (Fig 1.6). He also attempted to calculate the distances to the Moon and Sun, which, although still much too small, were more accurate than Aristarchus's values. He modified the standard Greek 'concentric nested spheres' model by proposing that the Sun and Moon moved around the Earth, which, although near, was not at the centre of the spheres. In drawing up his star catalogue, he devised a magnitude system to compare the relative brightnesses of the stars (see Chapter 7).

Finally, we come to Ptolemy, who worked around AD 140 in the Greek settlement of Alexandria, although his birthdate and nationality are unknown. He took the Earth-centred Aristotle model and endeavoured to account for the varying speed and occasional **retrograde** motion of the planets, as shown in Fig 1.7.

To maintain the idea that the planets move in perfect circles, he introduced a system of 'wheels within wheels'. He suggested that each planet

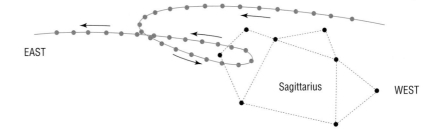

Fig 1.7 The planets can show retrograde motion – their track across the night sky reverses direction. This diagram represents the motion of Mars against the constellation Sagittarius.

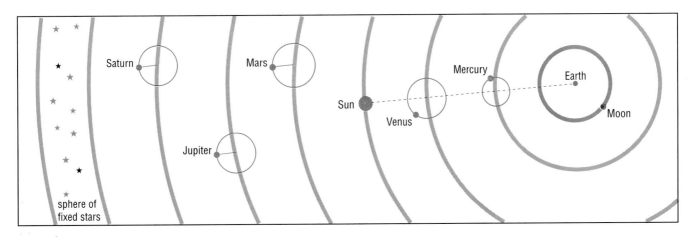

Fig 1.8 Ptolemy's model of the Universe. The planets move on epicycles, which allowed him to explain retrograde motion.

THE ORIGINS OF ASTRONOMY AND COSMOLOGY

moves in a small circle, called an **epicycle**, whose centre moves on a bigger circle called the **deferent**, as shown in Fig 1.8.

Most of Ptolemy's work was gathered into a book, now known by its Arabic title, the *Almagest*, which means 'The Greatest'. With Ptolemy's death, classical Western civilisation was slipping into the Dark Ages. In the 13th century, Europeans started to discover their classical heritage through Arabic translations.

Table 1.1 shows values for astronomical quantities as determined at the time of Ptolemy. Although they vary in accuracy, they stand as a monumental achievement to the observation and reasoning of these ancient astronomers.

Table 1.1   A comparison of Ptolemaic and modern measurements

Quantity	Ptolemaic measure/km	Modern measure/km
Earth's diameter	13 000	12 756
Moon's diameter	4300	3476
Sun's diameter	9×10^4	1.39×10^6
Earth–Moon distance	4×10^5	3.84×10^5
Earth–Sun distance	1×10^7	1.50×10^8

QUESTIONS

1.3 Look at the representation of the Ptolemaic model of the Universe shown in Fig 1.8. In what ways is it similar to our present-day view of the Solar System? In what ways is it different?

1.4 Look at the comparison of ancient and modern values of astronomical distances in Table 1.1. Which of the ancient measurements are most accurate? Which are least accurate? Suggest a reason why these measurements were inaccurate.

1.2 THE COPERNICAN REVOLUTION

A heliocentric model

The Ptolemaic model of the Universe was not superseded until the arrival of Nikolaus Koppernigk (or, in its latinised form, Copernicus) (1473–1543), the son of a rich Polish merchant (Fig 1.9).

Copernicus studied astronomy at the University of Cracow (1491–5), then at the University of Bologna (1496). In 1504 he returned to Poland, where he developed a **heliocentric** (Sun-centred) model of the Universe, as shown in Fig 1.10. In this model, the planets travel around the Sun in circular orbits. The model could explain the motion of the inferior planets (those nearer the Sun) and the superior planets (those further away than the Earth), including the **retrograde** (apparent backward) motion of these planets.

Copernicus was concerned that his ideas were in conflict with religious teachings, which assumed that the Earth was at the centre of the Universe. As he had strong links with the Church, he wanted to avoid criticism and possible charges of heresy. He therefore produced short handwritten pamphlets, which he distributed among scientific friends.

Copernicus's heliocentric model explained why the inferior planets, Mercury and Venus, always appear close to the Sun in the sky. This is because their orbits are smaller than that of the Earth. This explains why these two planets are only visible just after sunset and just before sunrise, whilst the superior planets can be seen in the middle of the night

Fig 1.9   Nikolaus Copernicus.

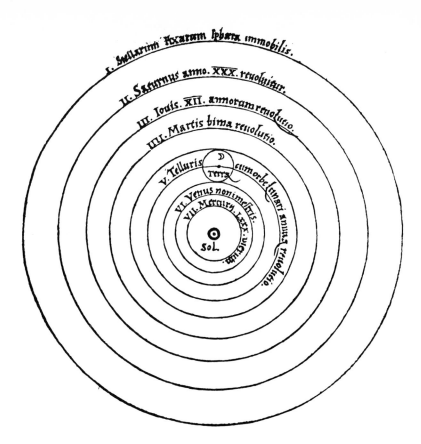

Fig 1.10 Copernicus's model of the Universe. The Earth (*Terra*) is just one of the planets that orbit the Sun (*Sol*). The stars form an outer, immobile sphere.

when the Sun is well below the horizon. Using this idea he used his mathematical ability to determine the orbital periods of the six known planets. (Uranus, Neptune and Pluto were only discovered after the telescope came into use.)

Despite the success of his model in describing some aspects of planetary motion, Copernicus realised that the perfectly circular paths of the planets around the Sun did not match with observations. He knew that planets do not appear to move equal amounts over a set number of days, and so he added epicycles to the path of each planet to take account of the slight variation in speed during its orbit.

Copernicus awakened astronomy from its dark age. All his ideas and calculations were finally published in 1543, when he knew he was terminally ill. The book was entitled *De Revolutionibus Orbium Coelestium* ('On the Revolutions of the Celestial Spheres'). It was written in Latin and contained mathematical and philosophical arguments that were beyond the grasp of most people. Consequently, the Church took little interest in the book and did not officially condemn it until 73 years later in 1616.

QUESTIONS

1.5 Mercury and Venus are the inferior planets – they are closer to the Sun than the Earth is. A consequence of this is that, when they are seen, they are always close to the Sun; they are never seen high in the night sky. Draw a diagram to explain why this is so.

1.6 Copernicus added epicycles to the paths of the planets.
(a) How could this account for their varying speeds?
(b) Why do you think Copernicus might have felt that this was an unsatisfactory solution to the problem?

Tycho Brahe

The years shortly after the death of Copernicus were to become a golden age for astronomy and cosmology, with three major figures who were to reshape our view of the Universe: Tycho Brahe, Johannes Kepler and Galileo Galilei were all born within a thirty-year period.

Tycho Brahe (1546–1601) (Fig 1.11), a Danish nobleman, was primarily an observational astronomer, having gained an interest in astronomy during his college days whilst studying law. He was an undoubted character; having lost part of his nose in a duel, he took to wearing false noses of gold or silver, which matched his outspoken personality. He made some important discoveries.

His first major contribution was the discovery of Tycho's Star of 1572, which was in fact a supernova (an exploding star – see Chapter 9), although this was not understood until comparatively recently. Classical theory held that the starry sphere above the planets was perfect and unchanging, so Tycho felt that this new star should be closer than the celestial sphere, and if this were to be the case he ought to be able to measure a change in the apparent position of the star between dawn and dusk. In other words, a degree of **parallax** should be apparent, even though the star seemed to move with the background stars. (There is a more detailed discussion of parallax in Chapter 7.)

Despite finding no parallax, Tycho published a short book *De Stella Nova* ('On the New Star'), which was sufficient to draw the attention of King Frederick II of Denmark, who provided Tycho with the funds to construct an observatory on the Danish island of Hveen. Although the observatory had no telescopes (they were yet to be invented), Tycho was able, using instruments such as the quadrant, like that shown in Fig 1.12, to measure the positions of 777 stars to remarkable accuracy. He was also able to measure the positions of the Sun, Moon and planets.

A later task was to revise the astronomical tables of the time. To do this, he required assistant mathematicians and astronomers, one of whom was Johannes Kepler. Tycho's last contribution was to ensure, shortly before his death in 1601, that his student was to succeed him as Imperial Mathematician, albeit at half the salary. Perhaps Tycho Brahe's most negative step was to return to the geocentric Universe; however, his precise observations and measurements were to be an immense help to Kepler.

Fig 1.11   Tycho Brahe.

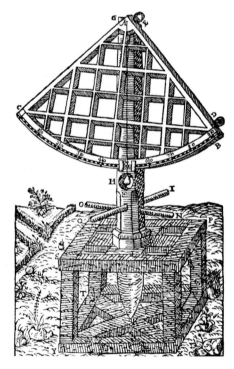

Fig 1.12   Tycho Brahe's wooden quadrant, an instrument he used for making astronomical observations.

Johannes Kepler

Johannes Kepler (1571–1630) (Fig 1.13) was born into a poor German family, and despite an unhappy childhood managed to succeed at a paupers' school, eventually winning a scholarship to Tubingen University. After university he worked on an almanac, which contained astrology and meteorology, in addition to astronomy. It was during this period that he prepared his first book, *Mysterium Cosmographicum*, which contained a long appreciation of Copernicus and his work, along with a theory of how the planetary spheres were separated by regular solids, with different numbers of surfaces and edges – see Fig 1.14. Although this latter theory was incorrect, it demonstrated Kepler's mathematical ability, and his wish to find a pattern for the planetary spheres.

By 1600 life was unsettled for Kepler owing to the persecution of Protestants in Austria. He had little hesitation in accepting an invitation from the eminent Tycho Brahe to join him in Prague. Unfortunately, Tycho Brahe died a year later. It was not long before Kepler put Tycho's obser-

THE ORIGINS OF ASTRONOMY AND COSMOLOGY

Fig 1.13 Johannes Kepler.

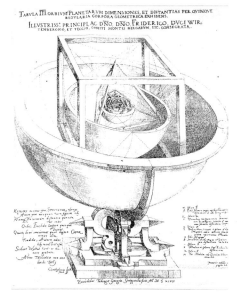

Fig 1.14 Kepler's model of the Universe.

vations to good use. In 1609 Kepler published his book *Astronomia Nova* ('New Astronomy'), in which he abandoned the 2000-year-old idea of perfectly circular orbits, with uniform motion. In this book, Kepler put forward two of his three laws of planetary motion.

Kepler's laws

Kepler deduced his laws from Brahe's precise records of the movement of the planets. It was a great achievement to be able to deduce three laws from this great mass of data. His first law can be stated as follows:

The orbit of a planet about the Sun is an ellipse with the Sun at one focus.

We now know that all the planets move in elliptical orbits – see Fig 1.15. However, it is worth emphasising that these ellipses are very close to circles, even for Pluto, which has the most elliptical orbit in the Solar System. Kepler deduced that the orbits were not perfectly circular from the fact that the planets appear to speed up and slow down as they travel round the Sun. (This had previously been explained by adding epicycles to their circular orbits.)

A planet moves fastest when it is nearest to the Sun. (This point in the orbit is referred to as perihelion.) Conversely, a planet moves slowest at aphelion, the point in its orbit when it is farthest from the Sun. After considerable trial and error, he came up with his second, 'equal-areas', law. This is stated as follows:

A line joining a planet and the Sun sweeps out equal areas in equal intervals of time.

This is shown in Fig 1.16. The planet takes one month to travel from A to B, and in this time it sweeps out area A_1. Now, if it also takes one month to travel from C to D, it will sweep out an area A_2, which is equal to A_1.

In addition to these two laws, Kepler also considered the force that holds the planets in place, and narrowly fell short of the idea of mutual gravitation. This would have been in advance of Isaac Newton. It is only fitting that Newton went on to verify Kepler's laws.

Kepler had established a milestone in cosmological progress. His was a stunning achievement when one considers that the most elliptical of the planetary orbits known to Kepler is that of Mercury, which has an orbit that deviates by less than 3% from being a perfect circle.

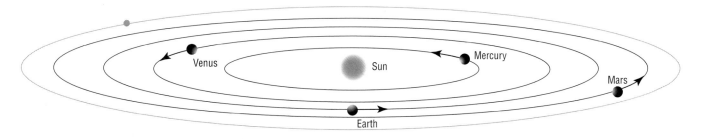

Fig 1.15 All planets travel around the Sun in elliptical orbits, in the same direction, and in roughly the same plane.

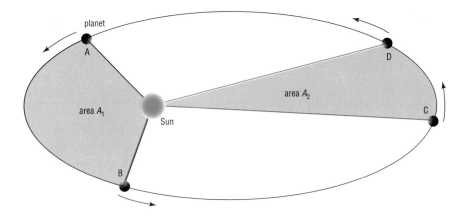

Fig 1.16 Representing the elliptical orbit of a planet around the Sun.

QUESTION

1.7 In Kepler's day, the concept of energy had not yet been developed. However, we can use this concept to understand the motion of a planet as it travels around an elliptical orbit. Fig 1.16 shows an (exaggerated) elliptical orbit.

(a) At which point is the planet moving fastest?

(b) At which point is it farthest from the Sun?

(c) Describe how the planet's kinetic energy and gravitational potential energy change around the orbit.

(d) What can you say about the planet's total energy?

Kepler's third law

Kepler kept writing and puzzling over the mysteries of the Universe, producing books on optics and Copernicus, the latter being widely read. However, his next significant work was *Harmonia Mundi* ('The Harmony of the World'), which returned to the theme of planetary motion. In this book he deduced the relationship between two quantities:

- The radii of the planetary orbits (their average distances from the Sun)
- Their orbital periods (the time taken for one complete orbit of the Sun)

This third law can be stated as follows:

> **A planet's orbital period squared is proportional to its average distance from the Sun cubed.**

Therefore if the orbital period is T and the average distance from the Sun is R, we can state the law as:

$$T^2 \propto R^3 \quad \text{or} \quad T^2 = kR^3$$

where k is a constant of proportionality whose value depends on the units in which T and R are measured.

On the basis of his three laws, Kepler drew up the 'Rudolphine Tables', published in 1627, three years before his death. These tables allowed astronomers to calculate the future positions of the planets to a high degree of accuracy. He left one further work, *Somnium* ('Dream'). This describes a journey to the Moon, and discusses the possible existence of lunar beings. Such imaginings would have been impossible a century earlier. The work of astronomers was bringing about a radical change in the way people viewed the objects that they saw in the night sky.

You can verify Kepler's third law by analysing the data given in Table 1.2. Note that Kepler knew of only six planets, as shown in the table.

Table 1.2 Data for planets in the Solar System

Planet	Orbital period, T/years	Average distance[a] from Sun, R/AU
Mercury	0.24	0.39
Venus	0.61	0.72
Earth	1.00	1.00
Mars	1.88	1.52
Jupiter	11.86	5.20
Saturn	29.46	9.54

[a]Note that distances are given in astronomical units (AU); 1 AU is the average distance of the Earth from the Sun.

1.8 Copy the table, and add to it values of T^2 and R^3.

1.9 Plot a suitable graph; what shape should you find to verify Kepler's third law?

1.10 Deduce a value for k from the graph. What are its units?

If you are familiar with the plotting of log–log graphs, an alternative approach would be to plot $\log T$ against $\log R$. In this case, the gradient of the graph will tell you the power relationship between T and R.

1.4 GALILEO GALILEI

Physicist and astronomer

Shortly before the birth of Johannes Kepler, another influential astronomer was born in Italy. He was Galileo Galilei (Fig 1.17), who was born in Pisa in 1564. Galileo was to be as important as Kepler in bringing about a modern view of the Universe.

Galileo contributed to many aspects of physics. He investigated, amongst other things, the speed of falling objects and the movement of pendulums. However, his first astronomical discovery related to the supernova of 1604. A **supernova** is a giant explosion that occurs when some stars reach the ends of their lives. Galileo became involved in a dispute with philosophers, as his observation was in conflict with the idea of the perfect and unchanging Heavens.

Galileo's name came to prominence again in 1609, when he built his first telescope following descriptions of similar devices constructed by Dutch lens-makers. The observations that Galileo made were to establish him as the first scientist to use the telescope. By the end of 1609 Galileo had managed to construct a telescope capable of 20× magnification, which enabled him to see the mountains of the Moon and the starry nature of the Milky Way (the band of stars across the night sky that we observe when looking out through the galactic disc). Both of these were included in his book *Siderius Nuncius* ('The Sidereal Messenger'), along with his major observations. In this book, published in 1610, he was brave enough to publish his observations and claim that they supported Copernican theory.

F.Villamœna Fecit.

Fig 1.17 Galileo Galilei.

The phases of Venus

Observing the planet Venus over a period of months, Galileo noticed two things:

- The apparent size of Venus varies.
- It exhibits 'phases' (like the phases of the Moon).

Furthermore, the size and the phase are linked to one another, as you can see in the drawings copied from modern photographs shown in Fig 1.18. (The 'box' in Chapter 5 explains the term *seconds of arc*.)

Galileo suggested that this could only be explained by a Copernican, heliocentric system. This model explained why Venus appears largest in its crescent phase and smallest in its full phase.

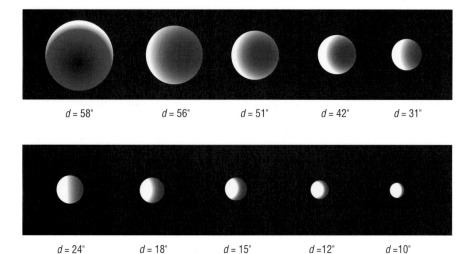

| d = 58" | d = 56" | d = 51" | d = 42" | d = 31" |

| d = 24" | d = 18" | d = 15" | d = 12" | d = 10" |

Fig 1.18   The phases of Venus – the appearance of Venus changes as it moves along its orbit. The planet's apparent diameter is given in seconds of arc.

QUESTION

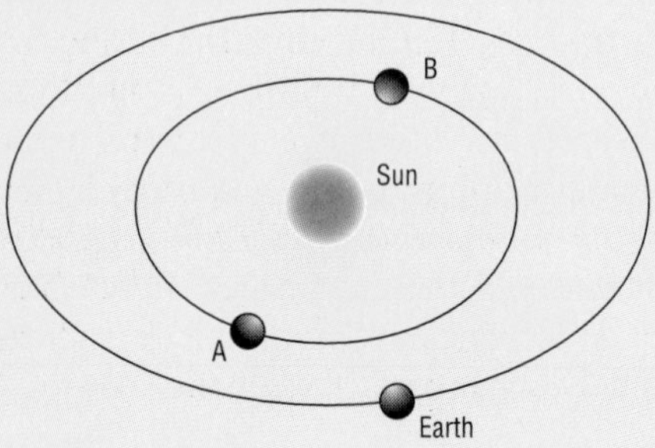

Fig 1.19   The appearance of Venus, as seen from the Earth, depends on its position in its orbit.

1.11 You should be familiar with the explanation of the phases of the Moon. You can apply similar reasoning to explain the phases of Venus. Fig 1.19 shows Venus in two positions in its orbit. When Venus is at A, Venus and the Earth are on the same side of the Sun. When Venus is at B, it is on the opposite side of the Sun.

(a) In which position, A or B, will Venus appear smallest, as seen from the Earth?

(b) In which position will Venus appear 'full' (i.e. fully illuminated by the Sun, as seen from the Earth)?

(c) Now write a short paragraph to describe how the apparent size and phase of Venus are related to its position around its orbit.

The moons of Jupiter and sunspots

Turning his telescope to Jupiter, Galileo noticed points of light close to the disc of Jupiter. Over a period of several nights he noticed that these followed Jupiter across the night sky; at the same time, their relative

Fig 1.20 Two pages from Galileo's book *Siderius Nuncius*, showing his observations of Jupiter and its moons. He identified four, but at times only two or three were visible.

positions gradually changed. These observations led him to believe that he was observing objects ('moons') orbiting the planet. His records are shown in Fig 1.20.

The more distant objects seemed to take longer to orbit Jupiter, so agreeing with Kepler's laws. Galileo had discovered the Jovian moons Io, Europa, Ganymede and Callisto.

Finally Galileo was able to observe dark spots on the surface of the Sun. The existence of sunspots, which had been familiar to Chinese astronomers for centuries, was a challenge to the idea of the perfect nature of the Heavens. The fact that they moved steadily across the face of the Sun also established that the Sun rotates on its axis.

Eventually Galileo's firm views on the Copernican system, along with his observational evidence, were to bring him into conflict with the Roman Catholic Church. In 1616 the Church issued an edict against Copernicanism, in effect banning Galileo from his astronomical work, although there were some members of the Church who maintained a friendship with Galileo. It was not until 1990, almost 400 years later, that the Roman Catholic Church forgave Galileo, when Pope John Paul II conceded that the Church had been wrong to oppose his scientific methodology and findings.

SUMMARY ASSIGNMENT

This chapter has looked at the work of some of the many astronomers who have changed the way in which we view the Universe. In particular, Copernicus, Kepler and Galileo made great contributions to the modern view of the Solar System.

Draw up a table to summarise their achievements. For each of the three astronomers, list:

- What observations they made (or used)
- What they deduced from these observations

THE ORIGINS OF ASTRONOMY AND COSMOLOGY

1.5 UNITS OF DISTANCE

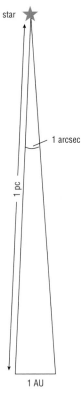

star

1 arcsec

1 pc

1 AU

Fig 1.21 An object at a distance of one parsec (1 pc) subtends an angle of one second of arc (1 arcsec) for a distance of one astronomical unit (1 AU).

Astronomical units, parsecs and light-years

In astronomy, we deal with very large distances. It can be inconvenient to quote these in metres; consequently, several other units are used. We have already met the astronomical unit (AU) above. Table 1.3 shows three of these units, and how they are defined. Table 1.4 shows how these units relate to metres, together with some relationships between them.

Table 1.3   Units of distance

Unit	Abbreviation	Definition
astronomical unit	AU	The average distance between Earth and Sun
light-year	ly	The distance travelled by light in one year
parsec	pc	See Fig 1.21

Table 1.4   Relationships between units of distance

$1 \text{ AU} = 1.496 \times 10^{11} \text{ m}$
$1 \text{ ly} = 9.46 \times 10^{15} \text{ m}$
$1 \text{ pc} = 3.086 \times 10^{16} \text{ m}$
$1 \text{ pc} = 206\,265 \text{ AU}$
$1 \text{ pc} = 3.26 \text{ ly}$
$1 \text{ ly} = 63\,240 \text{ AU}$

QUESTIONS

1.12 List these units in order of size, starting with the smallest: AU, pc, ly, m, km.

1.13 The Sun's nearest-neighbour star is Proxima Centauri, 4.2 ly distant. How far is this **(a)** in metres and **(b)** in parsecs?

SUMMARY

Historically, the Universe was thought to be Earth-centred (geocentric). The heavens were thought to be perfect and unchanging.

Astronomical observations proved to be incompatible with these views. Galileo's observations of Venus, Jupiter and the Sun challenged the idea of the perfection of the Heavens.

Kepler interpreted data on the movement of the planets to show that they orbit the Sun, confirming the ideas of those who favoured a Sun-centred (heliocentric) model of the Universe.

Kepler proposed three laws of planetary motion:
The planets move in elliptical orbits with the Sun at one focus.
A line joining a planet and the Sun sweeps out equal areas in equal intervals of time.
A planet's orbital period squared is proportional to its average distance from the Sun cubed.

Chapter 2

NEWTON AND AFTER

Until the time of Isaac Newton, physics and astronomy were separate disciplines. No-one imagined that the laws which apply to moving objects on Earth could apply equally to astronomical bodies like the Sun, Moon and planets. One of Newton's achievements, perhaps his greatest, was to unite these two sciences by showing that laws derived from terrestrial observations could help us to understand what was going on beyond the surface of the Earth.

LEARNING OBJECTIVES

After studying this chapter you should be able to:

1. state Newton's law of gravitation;

2. apply Newton's law of gravitation and the principles of circular motion to the planets;

3. link Newton's law of gravitation with the observations of Kepler;

4. describe how Newton's law of gravitation led to the discovery of Neptune.

2.1 NEWTON'S LAWS OF MOTION

Early days

Isaac Newton (Fig 2.1) was a remarkable man who was to make astronomy a truly scientific subject. His first remarkable achievement was to have two different dates of birth: 25 December 1642 and 4 January 1643! He was born at a time when Catholic Europe had adopted the Gregorian calendar, whilst Britain still used the much older Julian calendar. There was a discrepancy of ten days between these two calendars. In Woolsthorpe, Lincolnshire, where Newton was born, his birthdate was 25 December 1642; this was less than a year after the death of Galileo.

Isaac Newton was born into a farming family. His widowed mother initially hoped he would run the family estate on leaving school. However, such was the young Isaac's determination and interest in mathematics that he entered Trinity College, Cambridge, at the age of 18. Although he gained his B.A. degree in 1665, it was without distinction, and gave little evidence of the genius that was to emerge.

The catalyst that started Newton's memorable work was the Great Plague of 1665. Owing to Cambridge's proximity to London, the students were sent home for 18 months, until the University reopened. It was during this time that Newton conceived many of his most brilliant ideas. At the age of 26, he was appointed a Professor, and became a Fellow of the Royal Society at the age of 30. Soon after this he became Lucasian Professor of Mathematics, a post which three centuries later would be given to another eminent scientist, Stephen Hawking.

Fig 2.1 Isaac Newton.

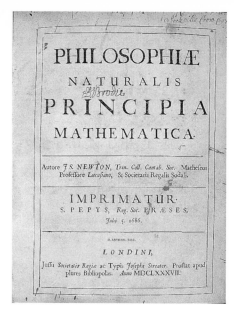

Fig 2.2 The title page from Newton's *Principia*.

Despite Newton's ideas and scientific precision, he was surprisingly reluctant to publish his works. Isaac Newton mistrusted many fellow scientists, becoming involved in major arguments in his later years. *Philosophiae Naturalis Principia Mathematica* (the 'Mathematical Principles of Natural Philosophy') was published in 1686, when Newton was 44 years old – see Fig 2.2. In this three-volume work, he set out the ideas that form the basis of what we now call 'Newtonian mechanics'.

This book contained his famous three laws of motion.

REVISION ASSIGNMENT

Newton drew on the earlier work of Galileo when he formulated the three laws of motion. Write brief statements of these three laws. (You may wish to refer to a core physics textbook.) In what sense can we say that Newton's second law is represented by the equation $F = ma$?

2.2 NEWTON'S LAW OF GRAVITATION

The falling apple

Everyone knows a version of the story of Newton and the apple – you can still see a descendent of the apple tree at his home in Lincolnshire. However, the idea that Newton saw the apple fall and said, 'Ah! There must be a force which makes things fall!' does little justice to his achievement. In fact, Newton's theory of gravitation did two things:

- It suggested that the Earth's gravity extended far beyond the Earth, to the Moon and beyond.
- It gave a mathematical relationship for the force of attraction between two bodies.

Newton sought to relate the familiar motion of objects falling on the Earth to the motion of a distant object – the Moon. He guessed that the Earth's gravity extended out into space, and that this was the force that kept the Moon in its orbit around the Earth. In the same way, the gravitational pull of the Sun kept the planets in their orbits. The gravitational pull of one mass on another, orbiting, mass provides the centripetal force that keeps the second mass in its orbit.

Newton had broken free from the idea that the laws governing the motion of the Solar System were unrelated to the laws obeyed by everyday objects on the surface of the Earth.

QUESTION

2.1 Which of Newton's laws of motion says that there must be a centripetal force acting on an orbiting body?

An equation for the force of gravity

Newton guessed that the force of gravity between two bodies must depend on each of their masses. Because the Earth has a large mass, its gravitational pull on the Moon will be significant.

He also realised that the force depends on the distance between the two bodies; the further apart they are, the weaker the force. In particular, he guessed that the pull of the Earth depends on the distance *from the centre of the Earth*.

He combined these ideas in his 'universal law of gravitation':

Two bodies attract each other with a force that is directly proportional to the product of their masses and inversely proportional to the square of the distance between them.

Therefore, for two masses m_1 and m_2 whose centres are a distance r apart (as shown in Fig 2.3), the gravitational force F between them is

$$F = -\frac{Gm_1m_2}{r^2}$$

where G is the **universal gravitational constant**. From later experiments, G has been found to have a value of 6.67×10^{-11} N m^2 kg^{-2}. The minus sign in the equation for F indicates that the force is in a negative direction when compared with the distance from body m_1.

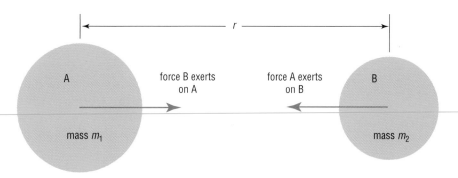

Fig 2.3 Masses A and B exert equal and opposite gravitational attractions on each other. The magnitude of each force is $F = Gm_1m_2/r^2$.

QUESTIONS

2.2 Use Newton's formula to work out the force of gravitational attraction between two books, each of mass 1 kg, lying 10 cm apart on a table. Comment on the magnitude of your result.

2.3 Calculate the force of gravitational attraction of the Earth on a student of mass 60 kg, on the Earth's surface. Comment on your result.
[mass of Earth = 6.0×10^{24} kg; radius of Earth = 6.4×10^6 m]

2.4 Calculate the force between the Earth (mass 6.0×10^{24} kg) and the Moon (mass 7.4×10^{22} kg) if the distance between the bodies is 3.8×10^8 m.

2.5 The force of the Moon on the Earth is equal and opposite to the force of the Earth on the Moon.

(a) Of which of Newton's laws of motion is this an example?

(b) Explain how this is 'built in' to Newton's law of gravitation.

ASSIGNMENT

How did Newton deduce that the force of gravity follows an inverse square law? He found supporting evidence from calculations relating to the Moon. Newton knew that the Moon was at a distance of roughly 60 Earth radii (see Fig 2.4) and he was able to show that its acceleration was roughly 3600 times less than the acceleration due to gravity at the Earth's surface. You can follow his logic, using the modern data given in Table 2.1.

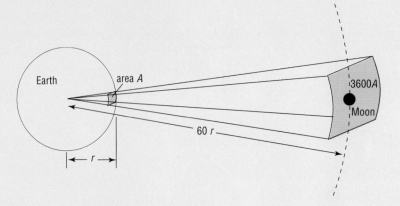

Fig 2.4 The Moon orbits the Earth at a distance of 60 Earth radii.

Table 2.1 Data for the Earth–Moon system

orbital period, $T = 27.3$ days
mean distance of Moon from Earth $= 3.84 \times 10^8$ m
mean radius of Earth $= 6.37 \times 10^6$ m

The Earth's gravity gives the Moon its centripetal acceleration. We can work this out from what we know about its orbital period around the Earth. We will compare this with the acceleration due to gravity that we experience on the Earth's surface.

2.6 Calculate the Moon's angular velocity ω, using $\omega = 2\pi/T$.

2.7 Now calculate the Moon's centripetal acceleration a, using $a = \omega^2 r$.

2.8 What is the acceleration due to gravity at the Earth's surface?

2.9 Now calculate the ratio of these two quantities:

(acceleration at Earth's surface)/(acceleration of Moon)

2.10 Calculate the ratio of the squares of the two relevant distances:

(radius of Moon's orbit)²/(radius of Earth)²

2.11 Compare your answers to 2.9 and 2.10. Do they support the idea that gravity obeys an inverse square law?

Gravity on the planets

Using Newton's law of gravitation, we can work out the strength of the gravitational field (i.e. the force on each 1 kg of mass) on the surface of the Moon or any planet. This quantity is often referred to as the planet's **surface gravity**; for the Earth, this is the familiar quantity $g = 9.8$ N kg⁻¹ (which when we write it in terms of the SI base units is $g = 9.8$ m s⁻²).

For a planet of mass M and radius r, the magnitude of the gravitational force on mass m is given by

$$F = \frac{GMm}{r^2}$$

and so the surface gravity $g = F/m$ is given by

$$g = \frac{GM}{r^2}$$

The surface gravity of a planet is therefore directly proportional to its mass and inversely proportional to the square of its radius. If we compare this with the Earth's surface gravity, we can find out how many times heavier (or lighter) one would feel on another planet.

QUESTION

2.12 Show that an astronaut on the Moon will weigh approximately one-sixth of his or her weight on the Earth.

[mass of Moon = 7.4×10^{22} kg; radius of Moon = 1.74×10^6 m]

2.3 NEWTON'S LAW AND THE PLANETS

In support of his law of gravitation, Newton was able to show that it was consistent with Kepler's third law. Remember that Kepler's third law ($T^2 \propto R^3$) was simply an *observational* law, which related the orbital periods of the planets to their distances from the Sun. Newton's law of gravitation was a more general law; the fact that it could be used to deduce Kepler's law was a great point in its favour.

Newton claimed that it was the gravitational pull of the Sun that kept the planets in their orbits. The Sun provided the necessary centripetal force. Hence we can write:

$$\frac{GMm}{R^2} = \frac{mv^2}{R}$$

where M is the mass of the Sun, and m is the mass of a planet orbiting with speed v at a distance R. Simplifying gives

$$\frac{GM}{R} = v^2$$

Now the planet's speed v is related to its orbital period T by

$$v = \frac{2\pi R}{T}$$

Substituting to eliminate v gives

$$\frac{GM}{R} = \left(\frac{2\pi R}{T}\right)^2$$

and rearranging gives

$$T^2 = \left(\frac{4\pi^2}{GM}\right)R^3$$

Hence we have $T^2 \propto R^3$, which is Kepler's third law.

QUESTION

2.13 Unfortunately, Newton had no way of knowing the values of G and M, so he could not calculate the value of the constant of proportionality in his equation for Kepler's third law. However, we now have an accurate value for G, i.e. $G = 6.67 \times 10^{-11}$ N m^2 kg^{-2}. Given that the Earth takes one year (3.15×10^7 s) to orbit the Sun at a distance of 1.50×10^{11} m, estimate the value of M, the mass of the Sun.

The discovery of Neptune

An outstanding piece of evidence in support of Newton's law of universal gravitation was the discovery of the planet Neptune in 1846. Prior to the discovery, astronomers had noticed discrepancies in the motion of Uranus that suggested that Uranus did not always obey Newton's laws of motion. It seemed to speed up and then slow down, with no apparent cause.

In 1843 the young British astronomer John Couch Adams began analysing the motion of Uranus. He guessed that the gravitational pull of an unseen planet was affecting Uranus, and by 1845 he had enough data to plot its position. He sent his data to the Astronomer Royal, but unfortunately little notice was taken of the information. However, on the continent, the French astronomer Urbain Leverrier had independently done the same calculations, which he sent to Johann Galle at the Berlin Observatory. When Galle received the letter, it took him only 30 minutes observation on that evening to find the planet. (Somewhat ironically, recent studies have shown that Galileo twice sighted the planet, in 1612 and 1613, but mistakenly assumed it to be a star, leaving the world to wait another 234 years!) A simplified outline of Adams' and Leverrier's reasoning follows.

All planets orbit in the same direction; the planets nearer the Sun orbit faster. Therefore, the planet Uranus will pass Neptune by 'overtaking on the inside', as shown in Fig 2.5.

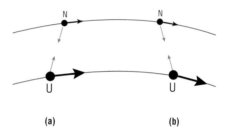

Fig 2.5 Neptune was discovered because of the effect of its gravitational attraction on Uranus. **(a)** As Uranus approaches Neptune, it is accelerated forwards. **(b)** Once it has passed Neptune, Uranus is decelerated.

As Uranus catches up on Neptune (Fig 2.5(a)), the gravitational force between the planets will accelerate Uranus forwards; similarly the (unseen) Neptune will be slowed down. Some time later (Fig 2.5(b)), when Uranus has passed Neptune, the reverse effect occurs. Neptune's gravitational influence will pull back on Uranus, slowing it down.

The essential points are:

- The force between Uranus and Neptune, though small in comparison with that between Uranus and the Sun, is still sufficient to produce distortions in Uranus's orbital motion.

- Observational techniques in the mid-19th century were sufficiently precise to allow astronomers to detect small distortions.

- Detailed calculations could be made with Newton's law of gravitation.

QUESTION

2.14 Uranus orbits the Sun at an average distance of 2.9×10^{12} m. At its closest approach, Neptune comes within 1.6×10^{12} m of Uranus. Show that the gravitational pull of Neptune on Uranus at this distance is approximately 1/6000th of the Sun's pull.

[mass of Sun = 2.0×10^{30} kg; mass of Neptune = 1.0×10^{26} kg]

SUMMARY

Newton's universal law of gravitation states that the gravitational force F between two point masses m_1 and m_2 separated by a distance r is given by

$$F = -\frac{Gm_1m_2}{r^2}$$

where G is the universal gravitational constant.

Newton's universal law of gravitation can be used to deduce Kepler's third law of planetary motion.

The period of a planet's orbit is given by

$$T^2 = \left(\frac{4\pi^2}{GM}\right)R^3$$

Further support for Newton's ideas came from the discovery of Neptune in 1846. The existence of Neptune was deduced from variations in the orbital motion of Uranus.

Chapter 3

EINSTEIN AND THE SPECIAL THEORY OF RELATIVITY

Many astronomical observations rely on light or other forms of electromagnetic radiation. In the 19th century, physicists were troubled by the question of how light could travel through space. And did Newton's laws of motion still apply to something travelling at 300 000 kilometres per second? In this chapter, we will see how Albert Einstein developed his theory of relativity to describe the mechanics of bodies moving at speeds approaching the speed of light.

LEARNING OBJECTIVES

After studying this chapter you should be able to:

1. understand the concept of the ether;

2. describe and understand the Michelson–Morley experiment;

3. recall and explain the two postulates of special relativity;

4. describe a thought experiment and a real experiment to illustrate time dilation;

5. describe a thought experiment to demonstrate length contraction;

6. appreciate the association between mass and energy;

7. explain why there is a finite speed to which a mass may be accelerated.

3.1 WAS NEWTON WRONG?

Many physicists in the 19th century were intrigued by the problem of how light passes through space. After all, sound requires the vibration of molecules of air (or whatever medium it is in), and will not pass through a vacuum. Similarly, transverse mechanical waves such as ripples on the surface of water require a medium in which to travel.

By the 1870s the speed of light had been established at 3×10^8 m s^{-1}, whilst physicists including Helmholtz and Maxwell had arrived at the realisation that light was a form of electric and magnetic interaction – hence the term *electromagnetic radiation*. Light travelled as varying electric and magnetic fields.

It is by no means obvious that electricity, magnetism and light are related. The discovery of how they are related was the work of several generations of scientists. Here are some of their discoveries (not in chronological order):

- A changing magnetic field induces an electric current in a wire.
- An electric current in a wire is surrounded by a magnetic field.
- A varying electric current in a wire produces radio waves in the space around it.
- Calculations show that a varying electric and magnetic field will travel through space at the speed of light.

These discoveries were made by Maxwell, Hertz, Faraday and Oersted. But which discovery belongs to which scientist?

3.1 Decide which scientist made each discovery, and put them in the correct historical order.

The idea of the ether

Although physicists had established that light is a form of electromagnetic radiation, they were unable to say how it got from place to place. To overcome this problem, they suggested that there was a medium (or substance) that supported the electric and magnetic fields. They called this medium the **ether**. However, having suggested the existence of this unseen ether, scientists then spent almost forty years searching in vain for a definitive proof of its existence!

It was believed that, as the Earth travels around its orbit, the ether wind would change – see Fig 3.1. The ether is stationary; at A, B and C, the Earth is moving in different directions through the ether. Now think about the light coming from a distant star. At A, its apparent speed will be increased, as we are moving towards it. At C, its speed will be reduced, as we are moving away. However, it proved impossible to measure these small predicted changes in the speed of light.

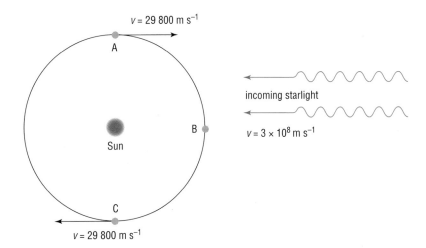

Fig 3.1 As the Earth moves around its orbit, at A it is moving towards the incoming starlight, and later at C away from it. Newtonian mechanics suggests that a change in the speed of light should be observed.

The Michelson–Morley experiment

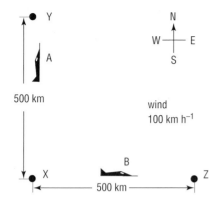

Fig 3.2 Which aeroplane will win the race?

Two American physicists, Michelson and Morley, devised an experiment that should have been successful in detecting the effects of the ether. Before describing their attempt to detect the ether wind, it is helpful to consider an analogy involving a race between two aircraft on a windy day.

Suppose two aeroplanes are to race along the course shown in Fig 3.2. Aeroplane A flies a return journey between X and Y, whilst aeroplane B flies the return journey between X and Z. Each plane is capable of flying at 1000 km h⁻¹, whilst the towns are 500 km apart.

If the race is held on a wind-free day, the result will be a tie. But if the race is repeated on a windy day with a 100 km h⁻¹ wind blowing from the east, the result will be different. A would always win. The reason for this is that B would spend more time travelling at 900 km h⁻¹ (1000 km h⁻¹ − 100 km h⁻¹) from X to Z, than travelling at 1100 km h⁻¹ (1000 km h⁻¹ + 100 km h⁻¹) from Z to X. Even considering that A would have to alter his (or her) bearing to compensate for the cross-wind, he (or she) always wins.

QUESTION

3.2 Use the data given in the example to find out the time difference between aeroplanes flying a return journey from X to Y and X to Z.

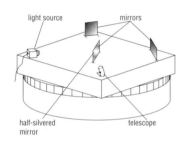

Fig 3.3 A simplified drawing of Michelson and Morley's interferometer.

Michelson and Morley carried out a similar 'race'. However, in their experiment they raced rays of light. They argued that, as the Earth moves through space, there would be a cross-wind caused by the ether, and that this would affect the speed of the racing rays.

Their experiment used a device called an **interferometer**, mounted on a massive stone block floating in mercury (Fig 3.3). They used a half-silvered mirror to split a ray of light in two, and then raced these two rays over paths at 90° to each other, just like the aircraft discussed above.

Fig 3.4 shows the paths of the two rays. A single ray of light is directed at a half-silvered mirror. This allows half the light (ray A) to go straight through whilst the other half (ray B) is reflected. Each ray then travels to a plane mirror, where it is reflected back along its path. Eventually both rays arrive in the telescope.

Michelson and Morley were looking for a difference in the time taken by the two rays to travel their equal distances. However, the high speed of light made timing impossible, so they used the fact that light is a wave.

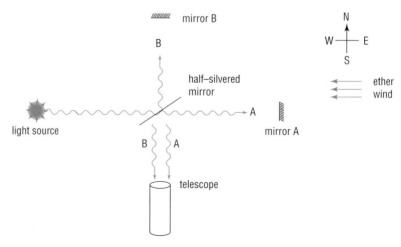

Fig 3.4 The paths of light rays in the interferometer.

EINSTEIN AND THE SPECIAL THEORY OF RELATIVITY

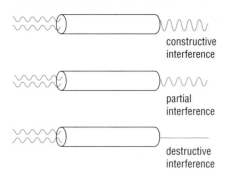

constructive interference

partial interference

destructive interference

Fig 3.5 The phase difference between two rays of light determines how they will interfere.

Looking into the eyepiece of their telescope, they hoped to see the effects of interference between the two rays.

If the waves arrived in phase, constructive interference would occur and they would see white light. However, if the waves were 180° out of phase, destructive interference would occur and they would see darkness – see Fig 3.5.

Now, suppose that the interferometer is initially positioned so that ray A is slowed down by the ether wind. If the interferometer is turned through 90°, ray A will no longer be affected, and it will be ray B's turn to be slowed down. Michelson and Morley argued that the result would be a change in the interference between the two rays, and so the brightness of the light seen in the telescope would change. As they slowly rotated their interferometer, they observed – no change!

This null result pointed to the idea that there is, indeed, no ether. The experiment has since been repeated several times by different scientists, with increasing precision. On no occasion have they found any evidence of the existence of an ether wind.

QUESTION	3.3 As the idea of the ether had become so entrenched, various reasons were advanced for its non-detection, other than the conclusion that it did not exist. One suggestion was that the Earth is fixed in the ether, and everything else moves with respect to the Earth and ether. Why does this seem unlikely?

3.2 THE PRINCIPLES OF RELATIVITY

Einstein's big idea

A dilemma existed: did the ether exist or not? If it did, why couldn't it be detected; and if it didn't exist, how did light travel through empty space? The solution was to be provided by the German scientist Albert Einstein (1879–1955) (Fig 3.6), with his theories of relativity.

Albert Einstein's father built up a business founded upon the recent discoveries of electromagnetism. He manufactured dynamos and electrical measuring equipment. It was in this environment that the young Einstein became curious about light. However, he was a far from exceptional student; he disliked the formal tutorial approach. He finished his education at the Polytechnic in Zurich (he had to sit the entrance examination twice), as without a diploma he could not go to university. Einstein's first stable job was as a patents clerk in Berne, Switzerland. This was an ideal post for him, as it allowed him the time to think about his ideas without the pressure to publish papers on a regular basis.

The idea of relativity developed from a thought experiment that was much discussed among physicists at the time. Consider an observer trying to see himself in a mirror; both the observer and the mirror are moving at the speed of light. Would the observer be able to see his reflection? The problem of what one would see in this situation was first encountered by the young Albert Einstein in his teens.

Existing theories predicted that the observer would not see his reflection, since the mirror would be moving away from the observer at the speed of light. The light from his face would never reach the mirror – see Fig 3.7. However, Einstein did not like this. He felt that the image ought to be seen in the mirror. Would the light from the observer's face really travel towards the mirror at twice the normal speed of light? Einstein thought not.

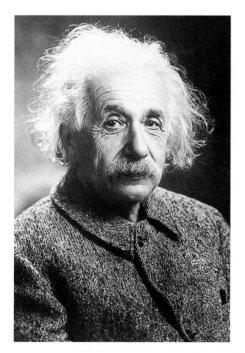

Fig 3.6 Albert Einstein.

Fig 3.7 Einstein looks in the mirror.

He published his ideas, which were to form the basis of the 'special theory of relativity', in 1905, as 'On the Electrodynamics of Moving Bodies', in the journal *Annalen der Physik*. These ideas were so radical that the paper contained no references to any other papers.

The postulates of special relativity

Einstein put forward two fundamental ideas (postulates) as the basis of his theory. Since then, these ideas have been tested many times and in many different ways, and they have yet to be found wanting.

> **Postulate 1 The speed of light is the same for all observers, no matter how they are moving.**

This means that, whether you are stationary with respect to a source of light, moving towards it, or moving away from it, the speed of light is always the same. (It doesn't appear to move faster if you are moving towards it, or slower if you are moving away from it.) In a vacuum, light always travels at a speed $c \sim 3 \times 10^8$ m s^{-1}, no matter what the speed of the source or the speed of the observer.

> **Postulate 2 All steady motion is relative, and cannot be detected without reference to an external point.**

You may have noticed that, if you are travelling fast in a train or aeroplane, it can be impossible to tell that you are moving. You can only detect *changes* in your speed or direction. (If you look out of the window, you can tell that you are moving – you are referring to an external point.)

These are the postulates of special relativity. The term *special* applies to objects that are moving at a constant velocity relative to one another, as opposed to the *general* theory, which refers to accelerated systems.

QUESTION

3.4 Imagine that you are in a spacecraft travelling at a speed of 10^8 m s^{-1}. (This is one-third of the speed of light.) You are travelling towards a star. You measure the speed of the light coming from the star.
   (a) According to Newtonian mechanics, what value should you expect to find for the speed of the light?
   (b) According to Einstein's first postulate, what value will you find?
   [speed of light in free space $c = 3 \times 10^8$ m s^{-1}]

What is a 'frame of reference'?

Imagine two passengers walking along the deck of a boat, as shown in Fig 3.8. Their walking speed is 2 m s^{-1} and the boat is moving at 10 m s^{-1}. (Note that these are both *steady* speeds.) Passenger A considers himself to be moving at 2 m s^{-1} (relative to the boat); however, an observer on the bank of the river would see the person moving at 12 m s^{-1}. An inertial frame is thus a non-accelerating frame in which we analyse the motion.

We must take care to specify the frame of reference in which we are making measurements, since one of the conclusions of Einstein's theory is that the results we obtain depend upon the frame of reference in which we are working.

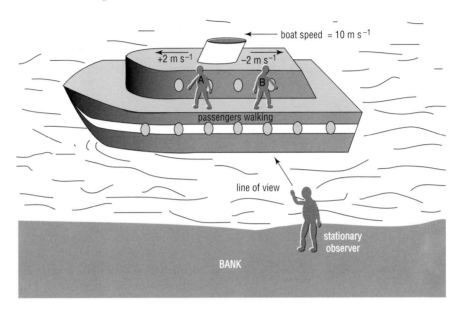

Fig 3.8   Illustrating frames of reference.

QUESTION

3.5 (a) What would be the speed of passenger B, as measured by passenger A?

(b) What would be the speed of passenger B, as measured by the observer on the bank?

Different times, different distances

Einstein's ideas radically altered our view of time, distance and speed. He showed that we cannot establish any absolute motion of an object; there is no stationary ether relative to which we can measure all motion. The one thing that is fixed is the *speed of light*.

An important consequence of this is that different observers in different frames of reference will make different observations of the same event. An example of this follows.

Consider a train moving along a track with a steady speed approaching that of light – see Fig 3.9. The train contains a lamp placed in the middle of a carriage with an observer standing next to it. Outside there is another observer, who is stationary relative to the tracks. The carriage contains a detector at each end, which registers the instant that light strikes that end of the carriage.

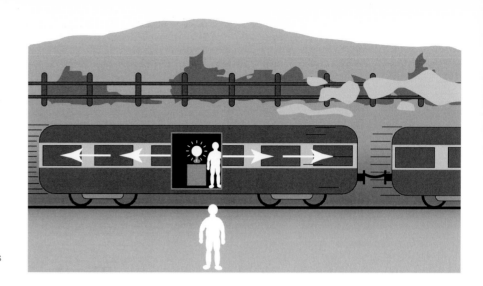

Fig 3.9 A very high-speed train can help us to understand relativity.

The person in the moving train will see the light strike both ends of the carriage at the same instant; as far as he is concerned, the light has to travel equal distances and so takes equal times.

However, the external observer would detect light striking the rear end first. The reason for this is that the external observer would see the rear end moving towards the light, so the light has to travel a shorter distance, whereas the front end would be travelling away from the light, giving a longer distance for the light to travel.

Many of the effects that Einstein predicted are only observable for objects moving at speeds approaching the speed of light – in other words, at **relativistic speeds**. In everyday life, we have little experience of this, and so we can get along quite happily with Newtonian mechanics. In the next sections, we will look at situations where the effects of relativity are more significant.

3.3 TIME DILATION

Take the slow train

What is time dilation? If a frame of reference such as a rocket travels at a speed approaching that of light, time appears to pass more slowly within that frame of reference. We say *appears* because this is what is observed by an outside observer. Within the fast-moving frame, time seems to pass at its normal rate. This can be seen in the following thought experiment.

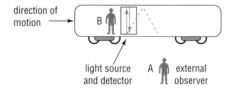

Fig 3.10 To the external observer, the light travels along a longer path than that seen by the observer in the train.

Consider the railway carriage again – see Fig 3.10. Inside the carriage is an unusual clock. This measures time by how long it takes for light to bounce up and down between two mirrors. The clock ticks every time the light bounces up and down.

For observer B on the train, the light is simply travelling up and down, and knowing the height between the mirrors and the speed of light, he

EINSTEIN AND THE SPECIAL THEORY OF RELATIVITY

can tell the time. The situation for the external observer A is different. Since the train is moving, A sees the light travelling a longer, diagonal, path along two sides of a triangle. Since the speed of light is constant, the light must take longer to travel along this path. So the external observer sees a longer time interval between reflections of the light; time appears to be running more slowly. This is called **time dilation**.

Einstein derived an equation relating the following two times:

- t_0 = the time interval of an event in the moving frame, as measured by an observer in that frame
- t = the same time interval, as measured by an observer outside the moving frame

The first observer is moving at speed v relative to the stationary observer. Einstein's equation for time dilation shows that the effect depends on the relative speed v of the two observers. (A derivation, based on Fig 3.10, is given in Appendix B.1.) The equation is:

$$t = \frac{t_0}{\sqrt{(1 - v^2/c^2)}}$$

The expression $1/\sqrt{(1 - v^2/c^2)}$ appears frequently in relativistic equations, and is often abbreviated to γ. So we have

$$t = \gamma t_0 \quad \text{or} \quad t_0 = t/\gamma$$

In other words, γ tells us the factor by which time appears to slow down for a moving observer.

The questions that follow will help you to interpret this equation.

QUESTIONS

3.6 (a) Show that, when $v = 0$, $\gamma = 1$.
(b) Show that, when $v = c$, $\gamma = \infty$ (infinity).
(c) Explain how this shows that there is no apparent time dilation for one observer who is stationary relative to another observer.

3.7 The faster an object moves, the slower time passes for that object, until at the speed of light time will appear to stop. You can show graphically how this happens, by plotting a graph to represent Einstein's equation.

Copy and complete Table 3.1, which shows the time which will appear to elapse when a stationary observer watches a moving object at different speeds, when 1 s passes for the moving object. This is calculated using

$$t = \frac{t_0}{\sqrt{(1 - v^2/c^2)}} \quad \text{and} \quad t_0 = 1 \text{ s}$$

Table 3.1

Speed v (in units of c)	Time interval, t/s
0	1.000
0.1c	1.005
0.2c	1.021
0.3c	...
...	...

Who's fastest?

Einstein's equation for time dilation shows that measurements of time depend on the relative motion of observers. If someone is moving fast relative to you, their clock will appear to move slowly.

Ironically, since motion is relative, the fast-moving observer will think that time is passing slowly for the stationary observer. This can be explained quite simply: we have no way of telling which observer is 'really' moving fast. We can only say that they are moving fast *relative to one another*. The problem in analysing such situations is that there is no absolute frame of reference against which we can measure all speeds.

This leads to the interesting 'twins paradox'. One twin sets off on a long journey through space at high speed. He spends an appreciable time travelling at a speed close to the speed of light. When he returns, the twin who was left behind is much older than the one who has been travelling. More intriguing still is the possibility of a father (or mother) who goes on a long mission, who on return discovers that their son (or daughter) is older than they are. This is science fact, not science fiction! However, it does not mean that high-speed travellers could journey back in time; it is simply that they travel into the future more slowly.

Einstein's ideas about time dilation are all very well in theory, but can their consequences be demonstrated in practice? Is there a real experiment to substantiate this effect? That is the subject of the next section.

3.4 TIME DILATION FOR MUONS

High-speed muons

In 1941 Einstein's special theory was used to solve a scientific puzzle. Muons are small elementary particles with a mass 207 times that of the electron. They can be produced in a particle accelerator, such as a cyclotron, where they are found to be unstable with a half-life of around 2 μs (microseconds) when at rest. Muons are also produced in the upper atmosphere by incoming cosmic rays, but because of their short half-life we would not expect to detect many of them at sea level. In fact, a substantial number *are* detected at sea level. Knowing the distance they have to travel, it has been calculated that the muons survive for 30 μs, about 15 times their measured life!

The explanation is that the decay process is slowed down because the muons are moving at relativistic speeds. It is as if each muon had a tiny clock on board. The average muon 'knows' to decay after 2 μs. However, when they move very fast, their clock runs slowly, and 2 μs to them is 30 μs to a stationary observer.

3.9 This question is based on an experiment carried out by Frisch and Smith at Mount Washington, USA, in 1963. They measured the rate at which muons reached the top of the mountain, and the rate at which they reached its foot. Of course, fewer reached the foot because many decayed before they got there.

Frisch and Smith found that the lifetimes of these high-altitude muons were extended by a factor of 15. In other words, for them, time was dilated by a factor of 15.

Using Einstein's equation for time dilation, show that the muons were travelling at a speed of about 99.8% of the speed of light.

[You will have to use the equation backwards, to find v.]

Atomic clocks

Time dilation was further verified in 1971, when two American physicists J.C. Hafele and R.E. Keating took very precise caesium atomic clocks on commercial jets. These clocks are accurate to 10^{-9} s in a year. After 45 h of flying they were able to demonstrate that the moving clocks ran slower than identical clocks left on the Earth.

3.5 LENGTH CONTRACTION

We have seen that Einstein showed that time is not an absolute quantity. If we measure a time interval, the result we get depends on the frame of reference in which we are measuring it. Time appears to run slow for an object that is moving fast relative to us.

Now, having established that time is not absolute, we can go on to consider what happens when we measure distances. Perhaps you will not be surprised to find that measurements of distance also depend on relative speed; they are not absolute.

We return to the thought experiment involving the train travelling along a railway line at a relativistic speed v, with a moving observer B and a stationary observer A, as shown earlier in Figs 3.9 and 3.10.

Remember that the centrally placed lamp appeared to illuminate the rear end of the carriage before illuminating the front end, when observed by the stationary observer. The length is foreshortened in the direction of travel. This effect is known as the **Fitzgerald–Lorentz contraction**. The apparent length of an object moving at a relativistic speed v is given by

$$l = l_0 \sqrt{(1 - v^2/c^2)}$$

where l = the apparent length of the moving object observed from the stationary frame (observer A) and l_0 = the length of the moving frame observed from the moving frame (observer B). Replacing $1/\sqrt{(1 - v^2/c^2)}$ by γ (as we did for time dilation), we can simply write

$$l_1 = l_0/\gamma$$

Here is another way to think about length contraction. Fig 3.11 shows a rocket sitting on the launch-pad. An observer on the ground can see that the rocket is 50 m long.

Later the rocket is travelling upwards at high speed, 80% of the speed of light. The same observer tries to measure its length. At the instant that the tail of the rocket is at the 200 m mark, its nose-cone is at 230 m. It seems to have contracted!

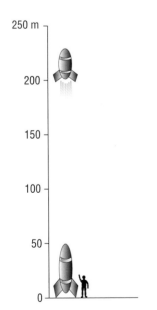

Fig 3.11 The apparent length of a rocket depends on its speed.

The reason for this is as follows. The observer makes both readings at the same instant. However, the light from the nose-cone has further to travel to his eye than the light from the rocket's tail, and so it takes longer to reach him. What the observer sees is the nose of the rocket at an earlier instant in time than its tail, an instant when it had not risen so high in the air. And so the rocket appears foreshortened.

This is not a problem for anyone who may be travelling in the rocket. For them, there is no foreshortening; the rocket is still 50 m long, if they care to measure it. But if they look back towards the launch tower, they will see that it is apparently foreshortened!

QUESTIONS

3.10 If it were possible to observe a 50 m rocket travelling past us at 80% of the speed of light, show that it would appear to be 30 m long to an external observer.

3.11 Sketch a graph of how you think the apparent length of the rocket in question 3.10 will vary as it accelerates from being stationary up to the speed of light. Check your answer by copying and completing Table 3.2.

How does this graph compare with a similar one for time dilation?

Table 3.2

Speed of rocket (in units of c)	Apparent length of rocket/m
0	50
0.1c	49.75
0.2c	…
…	…

ASSIGNMENT

You will have realised that the results of Einstein's special theory of relativity are quite difficult to grasp. In everyday life (and in much of physics), we can think in terms of absolute measurements of space and time. It is strange to find that, when we measure the length of something, the result depends on how fast it is moving relative to us.

Normally, we don't have to worry about the results of relativity. This is because we do not normally encounter objects that are moving relative to us at speeds approaching the speed of light.

There are several popular accounts of relativity, and reading one of these will help you to get to grips with the implications of relativity theory. In this assignment, your task is to find and read a simple account of the ideas of relativity. Two popular accounts are:

● *Mr Tompkins in Paperback*, by George Gamow (Cambridge University Press)

● *The Time and Space of Uncle Albert*, by Russell Stannard (Faber and Faber)

You may also find some more technical accounts, which include some of the equations we have discussed above. Appendix C lists some of these books.

Heavy going

Einstein went on to consider how his ideas about relativity would affect Newton's laws of motion. In particular, he tackled the question of Newton's second law, which we will think of as being represented by $F = ma$.

If we imagine applying a steady force to an object, the object will accelerate. However, as we have seen above, as the object goes faster, the apparent distances it travels will be reduced, due to the Fitzgerald–Lorentz contraction. Hence the force will appear to be having a smaller and smaller effect on the object as it accelerates.

One way to interpret this is to say that the object's mass appears to increase as it accelerates. Einstein deduced an expression to show how mass depends on speed:

$$ m = \frac{m_0}{\sqrt{(1 - v^2/c^2)}} \quad \text{or} \quad m = \gamma m_0 $$

where m_0 = mass of the object measured when it is at rest and m = its mass when it is moving, as it appears to a stationary observer. (The quantity m_0 is also known as the object's **rest mass**.)

Thus, as an object speeds up, its mass appears to increase, and γ tells us the factor by which it increases.

The questions that follow will help you to appreciate this effect.

QUESTIONS

3.12 Calculate the apparent mass of a 70 kg astronaut whose speed is:
  (a) 12 000 m s^{-1} (the maximum speed of the Apollo manned Moon mission),
  (b) 100 000 m s^{-1},
  (c) 10% of the speed of light,
  (d) 50% of the speed of light,
  (e) 99% of the speed of light,
  (f) the speed of light.

3.13 (a) This relativistic mass effect must be bad news to those people who run (or jog) to lose weight, as the faster they run the greater their mass becomes! What happens to their mass when they stop running?
  (b) Suppose we lived in a world where the speed of light was only 20 m s^{-1}. What implications would this have for someone who regularly jogged at 5 m s^{-1}?

Speed limit

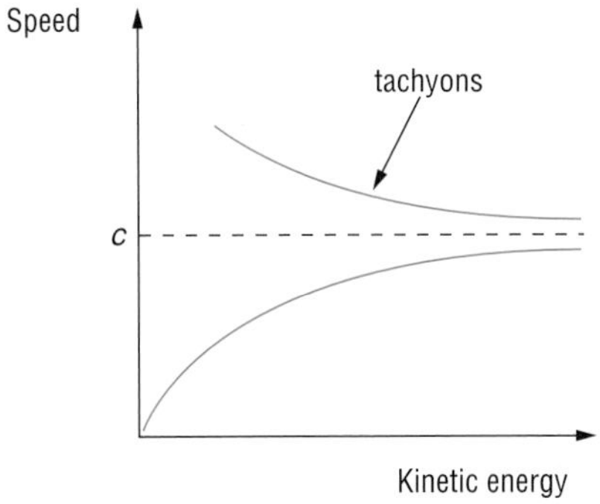

The increase in apparent mass of a fast-moving object has important implications. As an object moves faster, it becomes increasingly difficult to accelerate it. This means that to accelerate a mass to the speed of light requires an infinite amount of energy. This is why the speed of light has come to be recognised as a barrier; no object travelling at a slower speed than this can be accelerated to reach the speed of light.

It is beyond the scope of this book to consider the case of objects moving faster than the speed of light. However, analysis shows that, if such objects (known as **tachyons**) do really exist, they would experience a similar barrier; it would be impossible for them to slow down to reach the speed of light – see Fig 3.12.

Fig 3.12 The speed of light is a barrier that cannot be attained by objects moving more slowly.

The famous equation

Finally, to the most famous equation of all:

$$E = mc^2$$

where E is energy, m is mass and c is the speed of light. Einstein stated that the mass of a body is a measure of its energy. When we measure the mass of an object, we are effectively measuring its energy. The greater its mass, the greater its energy.

We can think of this the other way round: if we increase the energy of something, we also increase its mass. For example, there are two ways in which you could increase the energy of this book:

- You could lift it up, increasing its gravitational potential energy. Its mass will increase by a tiny amount.
- You could throw it across the room, giving it kinetic energy. Again, its mass will increase by a tiny amount.

These increases in mass are very tiny, and normally we are not aware of them. You can calculate the increase in mass, Δm, from the increase in energy, E, using

$$\Delta m = \frac{E}{c^2}$$

If you lift this book up a short distance, you might give it 1 J of energy. Its increase in mass is then

$$\Delta m = \frac{1\,J}{(3 \times 10^8\,m\,s^{-1})^2} = 1.1 \times 10^{-17}\,kg$$

and this is a very tiny amount indeed. (It is tiny because the value of c is so great.)

Mass–energy equivalence is more important on the nuclear scale – when the mass of a nucleus is compared with the sum of the masses of the individual particles of which it is made. For example, the nucleus of an oxygen-16 atom is made up of eight protons and eight neutrons. When measured, its mass is found to be slightly less than the masses of eight protons and eight neutrons added together – see Fig 3.13.

The reason for this is as follows. When the oxygen-16 nucleus formed from the separate nucleons, energy was released. So the energy of the

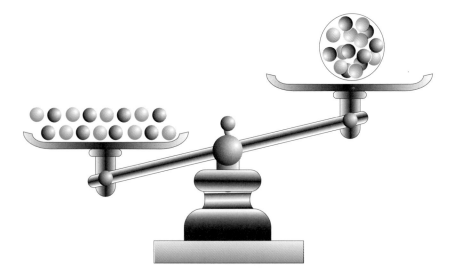

Fig 3.13   The separate protons and neutrons have more mass than the nucleus that they form when they bind together.

EINSTEIN AND THE SPECIAL THEORY OF RELATIVITY

nucleus is less than that of the nucleons from which it formed, and so its mass is less.

To dismantle the nucleus, we need to pull the nucleons apart (because there are attractive forces between them). To do this, we need to supply energy (do work). Thus, in dismantling the nucleus, we have to supply it with energy, and the mass of the nucleons increases.

QUESTIONS

3.14 If all of the mass of a 100 g apple could be converted into energy, how much energy would be released? Using this energy, how many 3 kW heaters could you run continuously for a year?

3.15 Calculate the energy released when an oxygen-16 nucleus is formed from separate protons and neutrons. Table 3.3 gives you the data needed.

Table 3.3

Particle	Mass/kg
proton	1.673×10^{-27}
neutron	1.675×10^{-27}
oxygen-16 nucleus	26.560×10^{-27}

SUMMARY

Michelson and Morley's experiment suggested the non-existence of the ether.

The special theory of relativity has two postulates:
The speed of light is constant for all observers, no matter how they are moving.
All steady motion is relative; there is no external frame of reference against which we can measure movement.

To a stationary observer, time appears to pass more slowly for a moving frame of reference.

To a stationary observer, a moving object appears shorter in its direction of travel.

The mass of a moving object is greater than its rest mass.

Mass and energy are equivalent; they are related by the equation $E = mc^2$.

EXAMINATION QUESTIONS: Theme 1

T1.1

Newton's theory of universal gravitation states that the force between two point masses is inversely proportional to the square of their separation, i.e.

$$F = \frac{Gm_1m_2}{r^2}$$

where G is the universal gravitational constant and equals 6.67×10^{-11} N m^2 kg^{-2}, m_1 and m_2 are the masses and r is the separation of the masses.

(a) Calculate the orbital speed of the Moon around the Earth given that the distance from the centre of the Earth to the centre of the Moon is 384 000 km.
  [The mass of the Earth = 6.00×10^{24} kg.]

(b) Calculate the time it takes for the Moon to orbit the Earth. (Your answer should be in days.)

(c) Explain why one side of the Moon is never seen from the Earth. You should make a numerical reference in your answer.

(UCLES June 1993)

T1.2

(a) The existence of the planets Neptune and Pluto was predicted before the planets were observed. Explain how this was possible.

(b) The Voyager missions launched in the 1970s made use of an unusual configuration of planets to facilitate a so-called 'Grand Tour' in which a space vehicle passed close by successive planets in turn during its journey out of the Solar System.
  (i) Sketch a likely shape for the trajectory of the vehicle as it passes close to one planet. Give your reasoning.
  (ii) Describe and explain the variation in the speed of the vehicle as it passes near one of the planets.

(c) Scientists are confident that many stars have planetary systems, despite the fact that these systems have not been observed.
  (i) Suggest a reason why no planets have been seen.
  (ii) What evidence is there that planets do accompany the nearer stars?

(UCLES December 1992)

T1.3

Thought experiments aid our understanding of Einstein's theories of relativity.

(a) Explain how real experiments and thought experiments differ.

(b) Outline **three** thought experiments which have been used to explain theories of relativity. State clearly which theory each experiment supports and what the experiment is demonstrating.

(c) Describe a real experiment which has been carried out to support one of the experiments described in (b).

(UCLES June 1994)

T1.4

Suppose that, in the future, mankind develops a rocket which is capable of travelling at 75% of the speed of light. This rocket has length 20 m and mass 1.0×10^4 kg. Einstein's laws of relativity predict various changes at such a high speed. Use the principles of relativity to answer the following questions.

(a) Calculate the length of the rocket as it would appear to:
    (i) person A, an astronaut in the rocket,
    (ii) person B, a stationary observer outside the rocket.

(b) A and B have similar watches which are synchronised as A passes B. Make appropriate calculations to enable you to comment on the readings of the two watches after A has travelled a considerable distance.

(c) Use the equation

$$m = \frac{m_0}{\sqrt{(1 - v^2/c^2)}}$$

to calculate the relativistic mass m of the rocket.

(d) The rocket burns fuel to maintain a constant thrust and meets negligible resistance to its motion. Comment on the factors governing the subsequent motion of the rocket.

(UCLES June 1992)

T1.5

(a) Describe the progress in the understanding of the Universe as a result of the work of Copernicus, Kepler, Galileo and Newton.

(b) Discuss Einstein's theory of special relativity. Your account should include:
    (i) the postulates of the theory,
    (ii) the consequences for our understanding of the physical quantities mass, length and time.

(UCLES June 1993)

Theme 2

OBSERVATION AND MEASUREMENT

The launch of the Hubble Space Telescope brought fascinating new images to our eyes. And yet, most people's view of the sky is with the naked eye. The development of telescopes was linked to our knowledge of lenses, which came from the development of spectacles in the Middle Ages. The need to capture permanent images brought about photography, and the need to transmit images brought the optical fibre.

The invention of the telescope accelerated the growth of our knowledge of the Universe – what we could observe became bigger and more varied. Discoveries were made across the electromagnetic spectrum, and these led to theories about the workings of distant stars.

To look at the night sky is to look back into history, as light takes over four years to reach us from Proxima Centauri, our nearest neighbour. We see galaxies as they were over a million years ago. Measurements of distance and time have become essential tools in understanding the Universe at large.

The Hubble Space Telescope has greatly increased the detail that we can observe in our views of objects in space.

Radio telescopes illustrate the way in which we can obtain different information about astronomical objects by studying their radiation in various parts of the electromagnetic spectrum.

Chapter 4

VISUAL DETECTION

This chapter looks at how light from the stars is detected and recorded by astronomers. The optics of lenses is covered in most A-level textbooks, such as *Physics* by Robert Hutchings, in the same series as this book. This chapter recaps the major points and then develops the ideas that are specific to astrophysics. The following chapters will examine the study of radiation (such as infrared) beyond the visible section of the spectrum, and how it provides us with information about the stars.

LEARNING OBJECTIVES

After studying this chapter you should be able to:

1. understand how optical devices are used to examine visible light;

2. describe how the brightness of an image in a camera is affected by aperture, exposure time and film speed;

3. explain how the depth of field may be varied when taking a photograph;

4. understand how photographic emulsions and charge-coupled devices detect radiation;

5. describe and compare refracting and reflecting telescopes;

6. discuss the applications of fibre optics in astronomy, medicine and telecommunications.

4.1 DETECTING RADIATION

Seeing stars

The most common method of observing stars is by the naked eye. Keen amateurs may use binoculars or a telescope. However, all the photographs in this book required more than this. Gone are the days when astronomers were a nocturnal breed. Modern astronomers may carry out some night-time observations, but much of their work is done by automated systems. Most observations are recorded electronically and displayed on computer screens, usually having benefited from electronic image-enhancing techniques.

Nevertheless, most amateur astronomers still use photographic film, as did the professional astronomer before the electronic age. It is helpful to look at the photographic aspect first before progressing to the modern-day techniques. Most of the objects that are photographed are faint, and so a long exposure is required. This introduces some difficulties.

Fig 4.1 shows a typical single-lens reflex (SLR) camera, which, although complex, can be simplified, as shown in Fig 4.2. Most cameras like this are capable of being used for astro-photography, although there are some

Fig 4.1 A single-lens reflex camera is a complex device.

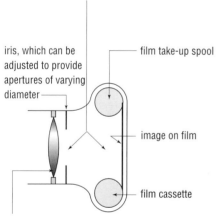

shutter (not shown) can be placed near the iris or just in front of the film

iris, which can be adjusted to provide apertures of varying diameter

film take-up spool

image on film

film cassette

lens on screw thread, so that it can be moved closer to or further from the film

Fig 4.2 This diagram shows the basic principles of a simple camera.

which may not be suitable. The requirements for taking astronomical photographs are as follows:

1. The shutter speed needs to be controllable, as the longer the shutter is open the more light gets in. In particular, it should have a B setting on the exposure time ring. The shutter will then stay open for as long as it is pressed down. In addition, it is convenient to have a wide range of shutter speeds, particularly those of a few seconds duration.

2. The aperture (or *f*-number) controls how much light can get into a camera. A good single-lens reflex camera may have apertures ranging from *f*/2 to *f*/22.

Aperture and *f*-numbers

The **aperture** is the opening of the lens through which light enters the camera. The size of this opening can be varied on all except the simplest cameras. Widening the aperture increases the amount of light let in, which is important if faint objects are to be photographed. The amount of light let in can also be increased by increasing the exposure time. Looking at the aperture ring, one sees the following sequence of numbers:

1.4 2   2.8   4   5.6   8   11   16   22

What do these numbers mean? The *f*-**numbers** (or focal ratios or stops) are altered by a diaphragm consisting of a number of overlapping blades. The smaller the aperture, the smaller the opening and the higher the *f*-number is. Strictly speaking, the *f*-number is a ratio defined as

f-number = (focal length of lens)/(diameter of lens)

and should be written as *f*/2.8, *f*/4, etc.

But what about this rather odd sequence of numbers? The pattern of numbers becomes clear if they are squared:

1.4	2	2.8	4	5.6	8	11	16	22
2	4	8	16	32	64	121	256	484

Each squared number is (roughly) double the previous one. The amount of light let in is proportional to the area of the aperture, which in turn is proportional to the square of the diameter, hence the 'square' relationship.

Fig 4.3 The depth of field of a photograph depends on the aperture (*f*-number) of the camera: **(a)** maximum aperture, **(b)** medium aperture and **(c)** minimum aperture. The depth of field is the range of distances from the camera where the picture is in focus. You can see the effect in these pictures by looking in particular at the trees in the background.

So an increase of one stop, say from $f/11$ to $f/16$, halves the amount of light entering the camera.

Finally the aperture affects the **depth of field**, as the three photographs in Fig 4.3 show. Notice that the minimum aperture gives the greatest depth of field with foreground and background both being clear. Whilst this is not a major consideration in astro-photography, it is important for photographers who wish to vary the subject of their photographs.

Sometimes a limited depth of field can be an advantage, as untidy or unwanted background detail can be removed. The aperture must then be large, and to limit the amount of light reaching the film a faster shutter speed is required.

Film speed

The photographic film plays its part, too. An image is formed on the film as a result of a chemical reaction in the emulsion when light falls on it. You may recall having the choice of 100 ASA, 200 ASA or 400 ASA films when buying a camera film. These are different film speeds, which describes how quickly the film reacts to light. There are two major systems, the American Standards Association (ASA) and the German Industrial System (DIN). These have been combined by the International Standards Organisation (ISO). So 200 ASA film, which can be described as 24° DIN, is now ISO 200/24°. The higher the speed the faster the film, which means that shorter exposure times are needed to make an image.

When considering astronomical photography, it must be remembered that the Earth rotates and therefore the sky 'moves'. If you have not got a motor-driven telescope for taking photographs, the exposure time will need to be comparatively short.

VISUAL DETECTION

Photographic emulsions

For most uses a monochrome (black and white) film is sufficient. At other times, photographs are taken through separate filters. A true colour picture is then made by combining the images produced in red, blue and green light.

Most photographic films have silver bromide or silver iodide crystals suspended in an emulsion. The emulsion covers either transparent plastic or glass, the latter being preferred for accurate spectroscopic work. When a film is exposed to light, the crystals in the emulsion undergo a chemical reaction, producing silver grains (which look black).

Light can be considered to behave like particles. It is the arrival of an individual **photon** (light particle) that triggers the chemical reaction. The speed of the film is related to the size of the grains. A fast film (one that reacts quickly to light) has a small number of grains, which are quite large (~3 μm), whilst a slow film has a large number of small grains (~20 nm). The disadvantage of a fast film is that it produces a coarser picture than a slow film, and is therefore unsuitable if details in the image are comparable in size to the grains.

For the film to be exposed, a grain may absorb as many as 10 photons before the silver grain will form. Furthermore only a fraction – perhaps 1 in 10 – of the photons are absorbed by the film, leading to what is called a **quantum efficiency** of 1%. Even the most sophisticated emulsions are limited to a quantum efficiency of about 4%.

If a film is exposed for too long or to too bright a source, it will suffer saturation. This is because too many photons arrive, and eventually there will be no grains left to react. The negative looks entirely black.

Finally, when taking colour photographs, the emulsion's response may not be equal for all parts of the spectrum. This can be compensated for with the use of a filter, where only a certain colour of light is allowed to pass through. Panchromatic film can be bought where the manufacturers strive to make the spectral response even.

QUESTION	
	4.1 You have been taking photographs of your friends in the garden. It is a sunny day, and you have used your camera with the following settings:

film speed: ISO 100/21°   aperture: $f/11$
shutter speed: 1/125 s   distance setting: 5 m

At night, the sky is still cloudless and you decide to try to photograph the Moon and stars. Explain how you would alter the above settings in an attempt to get clear images on the film. How would you avoid the effects of camera shake?

ASSIGNMENT	
	If you have the equipment and facilities you may like to try photographing the stars. You should experiment with the factors that affect the darkness of the image on the film; change them systematically.
	If you send your films away for developing, you should be aware that the film processors may think that some exposures are blank if you have photographed the night sky.
Safety note	Never attempt to photograph the Sun, because, when you look through the viewfinder, its light could be focused on your eye, and cause damage to it.

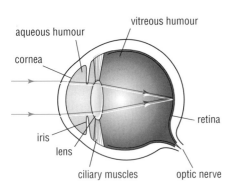

Fig 4.4 Light entering the eye is refracted several times before it forms a focused image on the retina.

The science of vision

The eye is similar to a camera, in that light passes through an aperture (the pupil) and is focused by a converging lens onto the light-sensitive retina – see Fig 4.4. Because the eye is a biological organ, it has some features that it does not share with a camera.

Light-sensitive cells

The retina is covered with cells that detect the incoming light. There are two types, whose names reflect their shapes: rod cells are sensitive to all wavelengths and allow us to see at night; cone cells are sensitive to different ranges of wavelengths, and allow us to see in colour during daylight. At night, because rod cells cannot distinguish between wavelengths, we only see in shades of grey.

Sensitivity

We need to be able to see in a great range of levels of light; we can see (dimly) by the light of the stars on a moonless night, and we must also be able to cope with the brightest sunny day. The range of light intensities in which we can see varies by a factor of perhaps one million million (10^{12})! The human brain could not cope with a signal from the eye which was millions of times stronger on a sunny day than on a dark night. To cope, the eye shows a logarithmic response to light intensity:

$$\text{response} \propto \log(\text{light intensity})$$

This means that the strength of the eye's signal to the brain goes up in equal steps each time the brightness of the light increases by a factor of 10. This is illustrated in Fig 4.5.

Quantum efficiency

We saw above that the best photographic emulsion has a quantum efficiency of about 4%; that is, about 25 light photons must enter the camera to produce one silver crystal in the emulsion. Equally, the eye cannot detect individual photons. Only about 10% of light reaching the eye gets to the sensitive cells without being absorbed or scattered. Then it takes between five and ten photons to stimulate a single receptor to send a nerve impulse. Overall, the eye's quantum efficiency is close to 1%.

Dark adaptation

You may have noticed that, if you walk from a brightly lit space into a darkened room, it is initially difficult to see anything, but gradually you can see more and more. Your eyes are becoming dark-adapted. It can take up to half an hour for your eyes to reach their maximum sensitivity in a

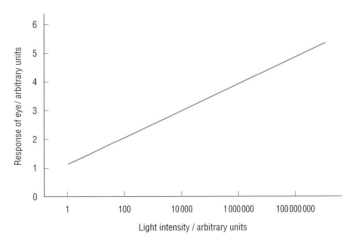

Fig 4.5 The eye shows a logarithmic response to the intensity of light entering it.

darkened place, as is shown in the graph of Fig 4.5. The rod cells in your retina, which have been over-exposed to light, are gradually recovering and becoming more sensitive.

Persistence of vision

Once an image has formed on the retina, it takes a fraction of a second for the cells to recover and respond again to incoming light. This is why, when the eye is presented with 50 pictures each second by a television set, we see continuous movement rather than a sequence of separate pictures.

QUESTIONS

4.2 Read the section above on quantum efficiency, and use the information to show that the quantum efficiency of the eye is 1–2%.

4.3 A camera is like an eye with a variable shutter speed. Explain how a camera can be used to produce clear images of the following:
(a) a fast-moving athlete who looks blurred to the naked eye;
(b) a faint star that is invisible to the naked eye.

ASSIGNMENT

Imagine that you were to photograph each of the following subjects:

- A head-and-shoulders portrait of a student in the classroom.
- A young child holding an ice-cream on a hot, sunny day.
- A fast-moving car from a distance of 10 m.
- A fast-moving car from a distance of 100 m.
- A person standing in the same direction as the Sun (but with the Sun out of the field of view).
- The Moon.
- A constellation in the sky.
- A planet such as Saturn.

Describe the arrangements you would make in terms of:

- The aperture (*f*-number)
- Focusing
- Speed of film
- Flash/no flash
- Use of tripod
- Any other requirements

If you have suitable equipment and facilities, you may like to try out your answers, and experiment with changing the factors listed above. If you send your films away for developing, be aware that the film processors may think that some exposures are blank if you have photographed the night sky.

INVESTIGATION

Design an investigation of the human eye's ability to adapt to the dark. How can you show that the eye's sensitivity gradually increases over a period of half an hour or so?
Equipment you might find useful: a luminous clock; a metre rule; a power supply; a torch bulb in a holder; etc.

Charge-coupled devices

In astronomy, light is at a premium. Distant stars are very faint – the rate at which light energy from a faint star enters a telescope may be as small as 10^{-12} W, and this can take a long time to show up on a photographic film.

One solution, of course, is to use a camera with very long exposure times. However, there are problems with this. The camera must be made to track the star as the Earth rotates; and expensive equipment may only produce one picture each day.

Astronomers looked around to find alternative methods for producing bright images. In the 1950s they started using photomultiplier tubes. Then the microelectronic revolution led to the development of minute specialised silicon chips. One such chip is the so-called **charge-coupled device** (CCD), which is now at the heart of every home video camera. It takes the place of the film in the camera.

The CCD is larger than many other chips, about the size of a postage stamp (typically 20 mm × 20 mm). The one shown in Fig. 4.6 consists of a silicon wafer divided into an array of picture elements (**pixels**). There are $800 \times 800 = 640\,000$ pixels in this one. Light falling on a pixel frees electrons, resulting in a small current, which can then be amplified.

So how do CCDs work? The following passage is adapted from an article taken from *New Scientist* (6 March 1986).

Fig 4.6 A charge-coupled device (CCD) is used to detect light in this astronomical CCD camera.

THE CHARGE-COUPLED DEVICE RECORDS A PICTURE ON A CHIP

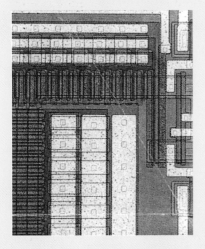

Fig 4.7 This photomicrograph shows the pixels at one corner of a CCD.

As the chip is made of silicon, a semiconductor, it does not conduct a current like a metal, but if the electrons in it are given enough energy to get away from their parent atoms they can move around. When a photon of light strikes a suitable silicon chip, its energy frees an electron. So an image of an astronomical object focused onto a silicon chip becomes an identical pattern of electrons within the chip. So how is the signal read?

The CCD's chip is divided into a large number of pixels (picture elements) each corresponding to a spot in the final image. The pixels are arranged in columns that are separated from one another by an insulator – see Fig 4.7. After a picture has been taken the accumulated electrons in the pixels of each column are fed out by passing them to an external circuit which amplifies the signals and feeds them to a computer. Here the image is stored in electronic form, until the astronomers wish to analyse it.

The pixel has two functions. As well as trapping the electrons freed by the incoming photons, it must be able to transfer the charge to the next pixel up the column, whilst simultaneously picking up the charge from the adjacent pixel down the column. The transfer of charge in this way gives the device its name.

The structure of a CCD is shown in Fig 4.8.

As with all the other detectors, the CCD has its advantages and disadvantages. On the plus side, it is relatively cheap because CCDs are used in television and video cameras, so there is a large market for them. The quantum efficiency is high at around 70%, which in turn leads to images being built up more quickly. The CCD can also be used for an exposure which involves light from faint objects, such as a distant galaxy. On the down side the CCD does not have the same quantum efficiency across the whole spectrum as the graph in Fig 4.9 shows.

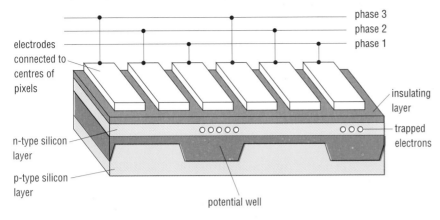

electrodes connected to centres of pixels

phase 3
phase 2
phase 1

insulating layer

trapped electrons

n-type silicon layer

p-type silicon layer

potential well

Fig 4.8 The structure of a CCD.

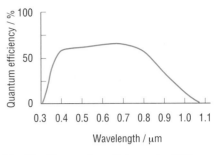

Fig 4.9 The quantum efficiency of a CCD depends on the wavelength of the light falling on it.

Also, it is difficult to produce a silicon without flaws in it. Even the smallest flaw can reduce the CCD's performance. In practice, astronomers buy a batch of CCDs and use those that give the best performance.

Combine a CCD with a space mounted telescope and you can realise how far we have come since Galileo discovered the moons of Jupiter and the possibility of Saturn having rings.

QUESTIONS

4.4 Compare the quantum efficiencies of the following: the eye, a photographic film and a charge-coupled device.

4.5 How does the pixel size of a CCD compare with the grain size of a photographic emulsion?

4.4 OPTICAL TELESCOPES

The advantages of using a telescope

If you look at the night sky it is possible to see the Moon, the stars and some of the planets. However, only the Moon will appear as anything more than a point of light. If you want to see details on the planets, or to observe nebulae and galactic spirals, a telescope is required. So what are the advantages of a telescope?

- Faint objects can be observed. To enable this, a large aperture is required to let plenty of light in. Also, a long exposure time is required. The eye cannot achieve either of these criteria.

- Measurements can be taken. The eye cannot make any observations other than subjective ones. A telescope can be linked to instruments that can be calibrated to take measurements.

- Telescopes can observe radiation beyond the limits of the visible electro-magnetic spectrum, such as the near-infrared and near-ultraviolet.

The Earth rotates, so a telescope needs a drive mechanism so that it can track a given star. Exposures are often of the order of minutes so that sufficient radiation can be picked up. Whilst the telescope may intensify the image, it is the function of the electronic imaging instruments or a camera to make up for the shortage of light.

There are two general types of telescope: **refracting telescopes** use lenses to focus light; **reflecting telescopes** use curved (usually parabolic) mirrors. We will look at these in turn.

Refracting telescopes

A simple refracting telescope (or refractor) consists of two lenses. Light from a distant object (such as a star) falls on the objective lens, which focuses the light to form an image. This is then magnified by a second, eyepiece lens. The 'size' of the instrument is usually defined by the diameter of the objective lens; typically, an amateur telescope may have a 75–80 mm lens, whereas the largest refractor built was the one at Yerkes Observatory in the USA, with a diameter of 101.6 cm – see Fig 4.10.

All telescopes aim to produce a magnified image of an object. To understand how this is done, we need to refer to Fig 4.11.

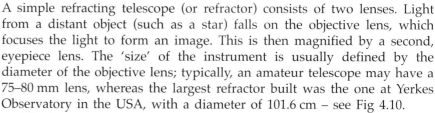

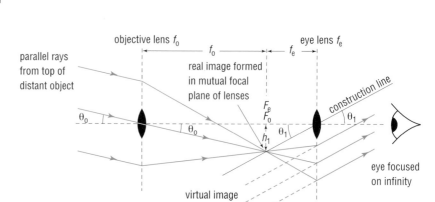

Fig 4.10 The Yerkes Observatory telescope – the world's largest refracting telescope.

Fig 4.11 Ray diagram for a refracting telescope.

Rays from the top of a distant object subtend an angle of θ_0 with the horizontal. Rays from any one point on the object are effectively parallel at the objective lens. So the objective lens forms a diminished real image in its focal plane. The eyepiece is used as a magnifying glass, with the final image at infinity when the telescope is in normal adjustment.

Now the rays from the distant image enter the eye at a greater angle, θ_1, and the object is magnified in the ratio of the two angles. The **angular magnification** M is defined as:

$$M = \frac{\text{angle subtended by image at eye}}{\text{angle subtended by object at eye}}$$

Hence, from Fig 4.11,

$$M = \frac{\theta_1}{\theta_0} = \frac{h/f_e}{h/f_o} = \frac{f_o}{f_e}$$

where f_o and f_e are the focal lengths of the objective and eyepiece lenses.

So to make the magnification as large as possible, the objective lens needs to have a long focal length whilst the eyepiece should have a short focal length.

From the ray diagram, you can also see that, in normal adjustment, the separation of the two lenses must be equal to the sum of their focal lengths:

$$\text{separation of lenses} = f_o + f_e$$

Magnification is not the only thing we require of a telescope. It must also have good **resolving power**, the ability to observe small or distant objects. This increases with the diameter and quality of the objective lens. The telescope must also give a bright image. This can be achieved by using a large objective lens, which will collect more light. A 10 cm objective lens will give an image that is four times as bright as a 5 cm objective lens, assuming the lenses are of comparable quality.

QUESTION

4.6 A telescope with an objective lens of focal length 3 m and diameter 40 cm can be used with interchangeable eyepiece lenses of focal lengths 5 cm, 3 cm and 1 cm. What angular magnification can be achieved with each eyepiece? How much brighter will the image appear compared with the naked eye?

[maximum diameter of pupil of eye = 0.5 cm]

The eye-ring

To gain the best results with a telescope, it is beneficial to have an eye-ring. This helps the users to position their eyes where they will collect most light coming from the objective lens. The image will thus appear brightest, and the field of view will be greatest.

An eye-ring is a circular ring or 'stop' of a diameter no greater than the observer's pupil. Fig 4.12 shows a ray diagram which explains how the position of the eye-ring is determined.

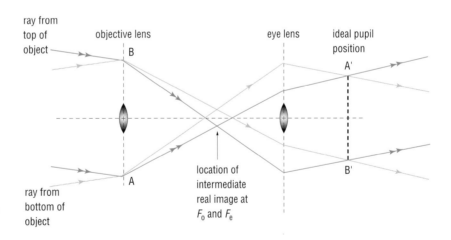

Fig 4.12 Ray diagram to construct the position of the eye-ring.

In the diagram, four rays are shown: rays from the top and bottom of the object, and passing through the top and bottom of the objective lens. The circular area with a diameter A'B' is the smallest area through which all the rays from the object are refracted by the objective and eyepiece lenses. To gain the best observations:

1. the observer should place his or her eye at A'B';

2. the telescope should have an eye-ring diameter A'B' equal to the observer's pupil diameter, approximately 5 mm.

From a consideration of similar triangles in this ray diagram, it can be shown that the telescope's magnification is related to the diameters of the objective lens and the eye-ring:

$$M = \frac{AB}{A'B'} = \frac{\text{diameter of objective lens}}{\text{diameter of eye-ring}}$$

4.7 A refracting telescope is made using the following lenses:
objective lens: focal length 50 cm, diameter 25 mm
eyepiece lens: focal length 10 cm

(a) How far apart should the lenses be positioned?
(b) What will be the magnification of the telescope?
(c) The diameter of the eye-ring is 5 mm. Explain why there would be no benefit in using an objective lens of a greater diameter – say, 50 mm.

Find a pair of binoculars. Hold them close to your eyes, and focus them so that you have a clear view of a distant object.

Gradually move the binoculars away, whilst still looking through them. Describe how your field of view changes, and how the brightness of the image changes.

(You can use a telescope for this, rather than binoculars, if you have one available.)

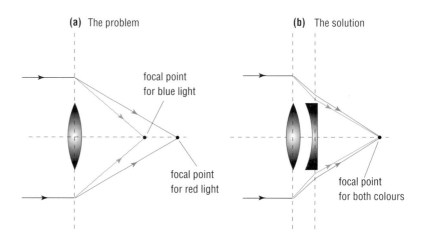

(a) The problem   **(b)** The solution

focal point for blue light

focal point for red light

focal point for both colours

Fig 4.13 Chromatic aberration can be reduced by the use of a matched pair of lenses.

The limitations of a refracting telescope

Nearly all professional telescopes are reflecting telescopes (which use mirrors), because of problems associated with refractors. Lenses refract light, and usually the different colours of the spectrum are refracted by differing amounts – Fig 4.13. This leads to an effect known as **chromatic aberration**, in which coloured fringes appear around objects when they are viewed. The problem is more extensive with larger lenses, as the largest lenses sag under their own weight. The 40 inch refractor at Yerkes Observatory (Fig 4.10) represents the upper limit of this type of telescope.

The problem of chromatic aberration can be reduced by using achromatic lenses, where all the colours are brought to the same focus. This is done by using several lenses sandwiched together, with up to four matched optical surfaces. This adds greatly to the cost of the instrument. Additionally, the lenses are not 100% transparent, so some light is lost.

Finally, the long focal length of the objective lens, which is essential in gaining a high magnification, increases the length of the whole telescope. (The Yerkes Observatory telescope is almost 20 m long.) This in turn requires a large observatory dome.

Mirror, mirror

Reflecting telescopes can vary in size and structure, with the common factor being a concave mirror. The photographs in Fig 4.14 show some small reflecting telescopes, as used by amateurs, and the giant 5 m Mount Palomar Telescope.

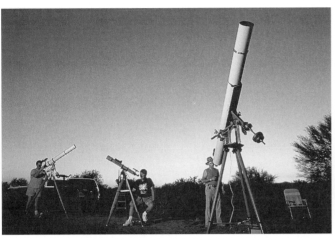

(a)

(b)

Fig 4.14 **(a)** Some small amateur reflecting telescopes being set up ready for a 'star party'; **(b)** the reflecting telescope at Mount Palomar.

In a reflecting telescope, parallel rays of light from a distant star are brought to a focus when they are reflected by a parabolic mirror – see Fig 4.15(a). The problem with this is that the focal point is *in front of* the mirror, so if you put yourself there to observe the image, you will block out the light. Different arrangements have been designed to overcome this: a second mirror is used to reflect the light out of the telescope tube so that the observer's head does not get in the way.

In the Newtonian system (devised, of course, by Isaac Newton), a plane mirror reflects the light out through a hole in the side of the telescope (Fig 4.15(b)).

In the Cassegrain system, the light is reflected back through a central hole in the parabolic mirror (Fig 4.15(c)).

Most large telescopes are reflectors, because a large mirror is much easier to produce than a large lens. The mirrors are usually made of glass with a thin layer of aluminium on the top surface to act as the reflecting surface. The large weight can be supported from behind.

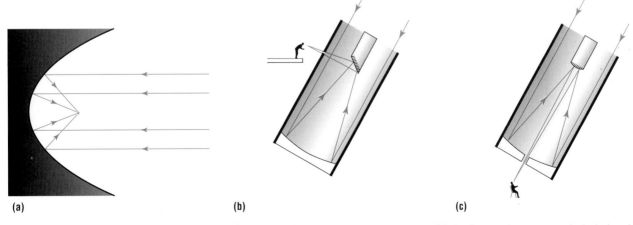

(a)　　　　　　　　　(b)　　　　　　　　　(c)

Fig 4.15 **(a)** A parabolic mirror focuses parallel rays at a point. **(b)** The Newtonian system, and **(c)** the Cassegrain system are both designed to make for more convenient viewing of the image.

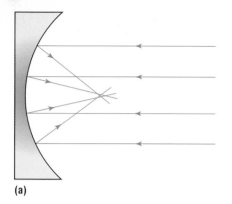

(a)

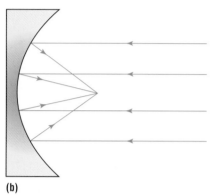

(b)

Fig 4.16 **(a)** A reflector whose surface is part of a sphere does not give perfect focusing. **(b)** A parabolic reflector has the precise shape needed to overcome spherical aberration.

Spherical concave mirrors are quite easy to produce. Unfortunately, they suffer from **spherical aberration**; that is, the parallel rays of light are not brought to a sharp focus. This can be overcome by making the central part of the mirror slightly deeper, forming a parabolic mirror – see Fig 4.16. Alternatively, on small reflecting telescopes, a thin lens may be added at the open end of the tube to correct for aberration.

Probably the most popular type of reflecting telescope is the Cassegrain focus. The William Herschel Telescope (Fig 4.17) and the Hubble Space Telescope are good examples.

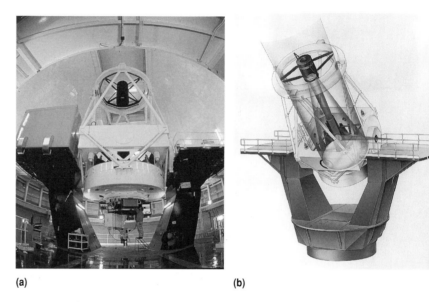

(a)   **(b)**

Fig 4.17 **(a)** The William Herschel Telescope at the Royal Greenwich Observatory in the Canaries. **(b)** A drawing to show how light is reflected and directed within the telescope.

QUESTION

4.8 Suggest reasons for the following:
  (a) The silvering of a telescope mirror is on the *top* surface of the glass, rather than the lower surface.
  (b) The Newtonian focus is popular for small instruments but not large ones.
  (c) A Cassegrain telescope (Fig 4.18) has a hole in its objective mirror but this does not affect the viewing ability of the instrument.

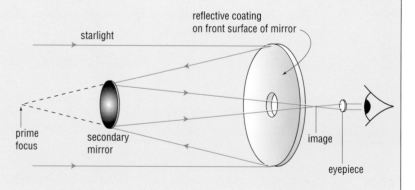

Fig 4.18 A Cassegrain reflecting telescope.

Fig 4.19 The Keck Telescope, Hawaii, has a reflector made of many separate segments. **(a)** A model and **(b)** a photograph of the principal mirror.

(a)   **(b)**

Grinding large telescope mirrors can take a long time and is an expensive operation. New telescopes are produced by spin-casting, in which molten glass is forced into a mould, thereby requiring minimal grinding. Another way of reducing costs is to use a mirror made in segments. Computers can then be used to move the segments so as to ensure a sharp focus. The Keck Telescope in Hawaii (Fig 4.19) is made from 36 hexagonal mirror segments. Each segment can be precisely positioned by computer control.

4.6 OPTICAL FIBRES IN ASTRONOMY

Total internal reflection

Optical fibres make use of a phenomenon called **total internal reflection**, which occurs when a ray of light is incident on the *inside* wall of a transparent fibre, as shown in Fig 4.20. Total internal reflection occurs only if the ray of light strikes the wall at an angle above the critical angle. The critical angle C is related to the refractive index n of the material by the equation:

$$\sin C = \frac{1}{n}$$

For a glass–air boundary, a typical value of n is 1.5, and the critical angle is thus

$$C = \sin^{-1}\left(\frac{1}{1.5}\right) = \sin^{-1} 0.667 = 42^{\circ}$$

In an optical fibre, rays of light travel along the fibre, bouncing repeatedly off the sides. If the fibre is bent, the light will follow its curvature.

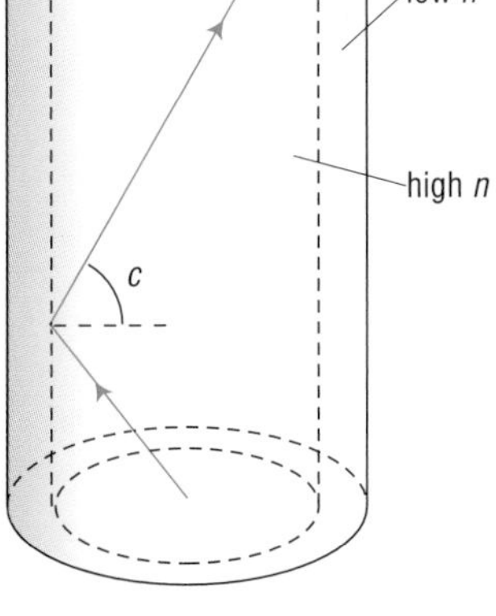

Using optical fibres

You have probably seen television documentaries where images are available from inside the human body; such photography is possible through the use of optical fibres. Hundreds of fibres are bundled together in an endoscope. Light is directed down some of the fibres, illuminating the area that is required for analysis. Other fibres are connected to a television camera, so providing an image on a television monitor. As the fibres are very thin (typically 100 μm), surgeons can make minimal incisions in a patient to insert the endoscope when carrying out internal examinations.

Telecommunications use more sophisticated optical fibres. There are two types of optical fibre, as shown in Fig 4.21.

Fig 4.20 Light travels along an optical fibre by total internal reflection.

low n

high n

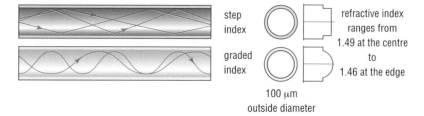

step index

graded index

refractive index ranges from 1.49 at the centre to 1.46 at the edge

100 μm outside diameter

Fig 4.21   Two general types of optical fibre.

- *Step-index fibre*   The core of the fibre is made of one type of glass; the outer cladding has a slightly lower refractive index.
- *Graded-index fibre*   The refractive index decreases gradually outwards from the centre of the fibre.

In a step-index fibre, light travels along, bouncing off the boundary between the two types of glass. A graded-index fibre is very cleverly designed. A ray of light along the centre of the fibre travels on a straight path. A ray that is not travelling along the axis of the fibre follows a curved path as it is refracted by the changing refractive index of the glass. You might expect the first (straight) ray to reach the end of the fibre first; however, the second ray travels further, but it also travels faster than the first ray, because it spends more time in the low-refractive-index material. Hence rays that start off together at the beginning of the fibre, reach the end of the fibre at the same time.

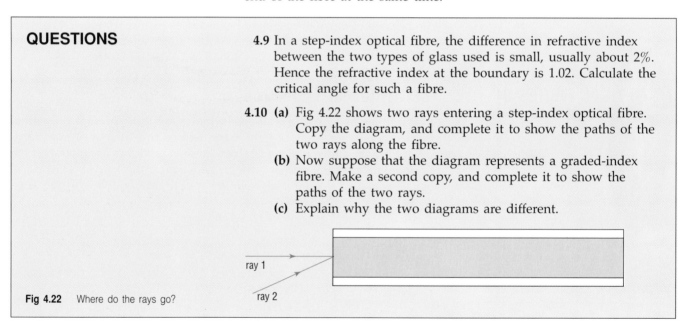

QUESTIONS

4.9 In a step-index optical fibre, the difference in refractive index between the two types of glass used is small, usually about 2%. Hence the refractive index at the boundary is 1.02. Calculate the critical angle for such a fibre.

4.10 **(a)** Fig 4.22 shows two rays entering a step-index optical fibre. Copy the diagram, and complete it to show the paths of the two rays along the fibre.
   (b) Now suppose that the diagram represents a graded-index fibre. Make a second copy, and complete it to show the paths of the two rays.
   (c) Explain why the two diagrams are different.

ray 1

ray 2

Fig 4.22   Where do the rays go?

Optical fibres versus copper cables

Prior to the development of optical fibres, most telecommunication signals travelled along copper cables. This has inherent problems. Although the resistivity of copper is low, it still has resistance, which reduces the strength and definition of any signals. To overcome this weakness, repeater amplifiers were required every few kilometres. Optical fibres, on the other hand, are made from high-purity glass, and signals can travel for hundreds of kilometres before they need to be re-amplified.

Copper wires are also bulky for the number of signals that can be transported, with a limit on how much information can be carried. Furthermore, by **multiplexing** (sending many pulsed signals along the same wire at the same time), many more signals can be sent simultaneously. Optical fibres are also much thinner. Finally, copper is more expensive than most of the materials used in optical fibres.

QUESTIONS

4.11 Why might optical fibres be more suitable than copper cables for cable television networks?

4.12 Why do you think videophones (telephones that show the image of the person at the other end) have only recently been technologically possible? What factors would affect whether the videophone is a financial success for its maker? What factors would affect your choice as to whether you would buy one?

Optical fibres in astronomy

Just as fibres are bundled in an endoscope (for medical observations) they can be bundled together for astronomical uses. One such arrangement is shown in Fig 4.23.

The block of fibres is placed at the focus of a telescope. An image of part of the night sky falls on the block, so that each fibre receives light from the stars in a different part of the image. The fibres then lead the light away to where it can be analysed.

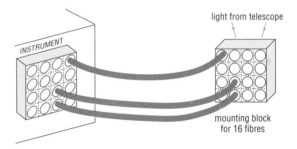

Fig 4.23 Optical fibres carry starlight from the focal plane of a telescope to other instruments, where it can be analysed.

The advantage of this technique is that the light from several stars or galaxies may be studied simultaneously, without any adjustment to the alignment of the telescope. This can be very useful when analysing the red-shifts of individual galaxies within a distant cluster of galaxies, or analysing the spectra of the light from stars in a closely packed cluster.

SUMMARY

The intensity of the image formed on a photographic film depends on the aperture, the exposure time and the speed of the film.

The eye has a logarithmic response to the intensity of light, so that it can respond to a wide range of light levels.

Quantum efficiencies: the eye – around 1%; photographic film – around 4%; charge-coupled device (CCD) – 70%.

There are two main types of telescope, refracting and reflecting.

The angular magnification of a refracting telescope is related to the focal lengths of the two lenses:

$$M = \frac{f_o}{f_e}$$

Reflectors are preferred for large telescopes, as they have fewer limitations.

Optical fibres can be used to transmit light over long distances, and to carry light between astronomical instruments.

Chapter 5

A LIMITED VIEW

We find out about the stars and other objects in space by studying the light (and other electromagnetic radiation) that we receive from them. However, we can never have a 'perfect view' – there are three stages through which the light must go before we have a final image, and the image of a star can become degraded at each stage. This chapter looks in turn at these three stages:

- The light from a star must reach us through the Earth's atmosphere, and is affected by this.
- The light then enters an optical instrument – a telescope, or an eye. Any such instrument has its limitations.
- Finally, the image is detected and recorded, perhaps by a photographic film or a charge-coupled device. Again, these have their limitations.

By understanding each of these stages, we can find out how to produce improved images of the objects that are of interest to astronomers.

LEARNING OBJECTIVES

After studying this chapter you should be able to:

1. discuss the factors that limit the clarity of images of stars and other astronomical objects;

2. understand how diffraction and interference effects can limit the resolving power of optical and radio telescopes;

3. discuss the effects that the Earth's atmosphere has on electromagnetic radiation;

4. understand the main principles of radio-astronomy;

5. discuss the economic considerations involved in astronomy research.

5.1 RESOLVING POWER

One into two

Imagine looking at a distant car at night. At first, you can only see a single bright blob – its headlights. Now, as the car approaches, this single blob splits into two, and you can distinguish both headlights. At first, you were unable to **resolve** the lights, because they were too close together in your field of view.

Resolving power is a measure of how good your eyes (or an optical instrument) are at seeing as separate two objects that are close together. For the example of the car, the two lights might be 1.5 m apart, and we might find that (with good eyesight and in clear conditions) our eyes can see them as separate at a distance of 5 km.

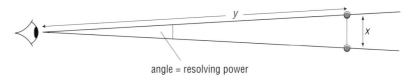

Fig 5.1 Defining resolving power.

In practice, resolving power is given as an angle, as shown in Fig 5.1. Two objects, separated by a distance x, can just be distinguished at a distance y. Then the resolving power is given by

$$\text{resolving power} = \frac{x}{y}$$

For the example above of the car headlights, we have

$$\text{resolving power of eye} = \frac{1.5\,\text{m}}{5000\,\text{m}} = 3 \times 10^{-4}\,\text{rad}$$

Note that, since resolving power is an angle, its units are radians (or other units of angle). If you are not familiar with these units, see the note in the box on the next page.

You can investigate the resolving power of your own eye by following the instructions below.

INVESTIGATION

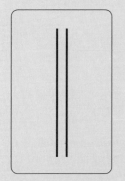

Fig 5.2 Two parallel lines for determining your own resolving power.

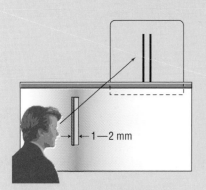

Fig 5.3 Viewing the lines through an opening.

On a piece of white paper or card, draw two parallel lines with a black pencil, a few millimetres apart, as shown in Fig 5.2. When viewed from close to, these lines are separable; however, at a distance they are not.

Stick your card or paper to a wall at the end of a long room or corridor. Walk towards the lines, and stop at the point where you can just resolve them.

Measure the separation of the lines, and your distance from them. Calculate the resolving power of your eye.

Try repeating the experiment with different separations for the lines. Do you always find the same result (within experimental uncertainty)?

Now repeat the experiment when looking through a narrow slit in a piece of card, as shown in Fig 5.3. What do you notice?

You can extend this investigation to find out how the resolving power of your eye depends on the wavelength of the light that you are observing. Set up the multiple light source shown in Fig 5.4. Hold a green filter in front of your eye. Determine how close you must stand to resolve the individual lamps.

Repeat the experiment with red and blue filters. How does the resolving power of your eye depend on the colour of the light?

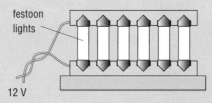

Fig 5.4 Festoon lamps provide a multiple source of light.

NOTE ON MEASURING ANGLES

The two most-used units for measuring angles are **radians** and **degrees**. You should be familar with both of these, and know how to convert between them.

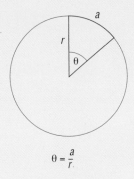

$$\theta = \frac{a}{r}$$

Fig 5.5 Defining the measurement of an angle in radians.

Fig 5.5 shows how the angle θ is defined in radians.

$$\theta = \frac{\text{length of arc}}{\text{radius}} = \frac{a}{r}$$

In a full circle, there are 2π radians or $360°$. It follows that, to convert from radians to degrees, we must multiply by the factor $360/2\pi$.

In addition, degrees are subdivided into minutes (arcmin) and seconds (arcsec):

$$60 \text{ arcsec} = 1 \text{ arcmin}$$
$$60 \text{ arcmin} = 1 \text{ degree}$$

QUESTIONS

5.1 (a) The Moon is at a distance of 3.84×10^5 km from the Earth. Its diameter is 3480 km. Calculate the angle that the Moon subtends at the Earth, in radians and in degrees.

(b) The Sun is at a distance of 1.5×10^8 km from the Earth. It subtends the same angle as the Moon, at the Earth. Calculate the diameter of the Sun.

5.2 The resolving power of the eye is approximately 3×10^{-4} rad. Show that this is approximately equal to 1 arcmin.

5.2 THE TURBULENT ATMOSPHERE

Twinkling stars

> Twinkle, twinkle, little star,
> How I wonder what you are!

Most of us are familiar with the opening lines of this childhood nursery rhyme. But why *do* stars twinkle?

Our atmosphere is turbulent. It consists of moving bodies of air. Warmer air rises to form a convection current. Furthermore, this air is less dense than surrounding air and therefore has a lower refractive index. The result is that, as rays of light pass through the atmosphere, they are deviated – see Fig 5.6. As the regions of different densities move across in front of a

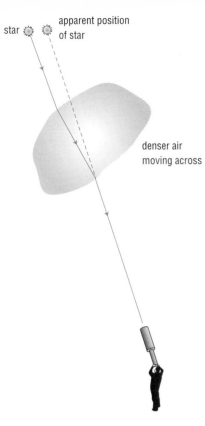

star apparent position
of star

denser air
moving across

Fig 5.6 A moving region of different density in the atmosphere deflects starlight, so that the star appears to twinkle.

star, its light is deflected, and its apparent position changes. This is why stars appear to twinkle – they show **scintillation**. To reduce the effect, many major observatories are sited on mountain peaks, including those at Mauna Kea, Kitt Peak and Mount Palomar.

The density of the atmosphere varies over a scale of a few metres. Our view of stars is as if we were looking through frosted glass, with a pattern that varies on this scale. For our eyes, this is not too serious; the 'frosting' does not vary much across the diameter of our pupil. However, things are much more serious for large telescopes, whose resolving power may be severely limited by these variations in refractive index.

The improved resolution that can be achieved by operating a telescope in space is shown in Table 5.1.

Table 5.1 Improvement in resolving power – viewing from above the atmosphere

	Viewing from Earth's surface	Viewing from space
eye (3 mm pupil)	60 arcsec	40 arcsec
telescope (5 m objective)	1 arcsec	0.02 arcsec

QUESTIONS

5.3 Explain why the improvement in resolving power shown in Table 5.1 is much greater for a telescope than for the eye.

5.4 It is sometimes suggested that one can distinguish planets from stars because planets do not twinkle. This is not strictly true; however, it is true that one of the closer planets, such as Mars, will twinkle less noticeably than a star, as the following calculation shows.

(a) On a particular night, Mars is at a distance of 7.5×10^7 km from Earth. Its diameter is 6800 km. Calculate the angle (in radians) that Mars subtends at the eye of an observer.

(b) Suppose that the light from Mars passes through the atmosphere in a region 10 km up, where regions of different density have a typical diameter of 0.5 m. Calculate the angle subtended by such a region at the eye of an observer on the Earth's surface.

(c) Compare your two answers. Why does this suggest that the light from Mars will be less twinkly than starlight?

The opaque atmosphere

It is very easy to assume that the atmosphere is transparent since we can see the Sun by day and the stars at night. Of course, our eyes see only a small part of the electromagnetic spectrum, and the atmosphere has a different effect at other wavelengths. You may be aware that some radio

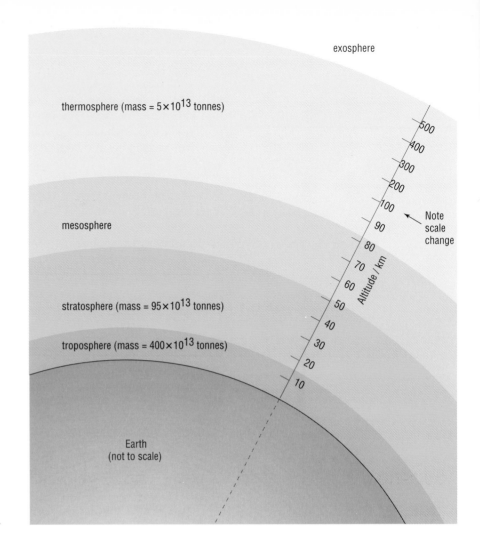

exosphere

thermosphere (mass = 5×10^{13} tonnes)

mesosphere

stratosphere (mass = 95×10^{13} tonnes)

troposphere (mass = 400×10^{13} tonnes)

Note scale change

Altitude / km

500
400
300
200
100
90
80
70
60
50
40
30
20
10

Earth
(not to scale)

Fig 5.7 The layers of the atmosphere.

waves can be reflected off the ionosphere (one of the layers of our atmosphere), whilst problems associated with the 'hole in the ozone layer' remind us of the dangers of ultraviolet radiation if we do not have an ozone barrier.

The atmosphere can be considered to be made up of five layers, as shown in Fig 5.7. These layers are the following:

- The **troposphere** – This is the surface layer of the atmosphere, which contains 75% of the air mass of our planet. It extends to a height of about 15 km. It also contains most of the water vapour; changes in the troposphere account for most of the weather on Earth. The temperature of the troposphere decreases with height above the Earth.

- The **stratosphere** – This layer extends up to a height of 50 km. It is this layer that contains ozone (at a height of about 30 km). The stratosphere shows a rise in temperature with increasing height. The ozone absorbs solar energy in the ultraviolet region. Without this filter, there would be no life on the Earth.

- The **mesosphere** – This is a layer between 50 and 80 km above the Earth's surface. The atmospheric temperature again decreases with increasing height.

- The **thermosphere** – As the name suggests, this layer has a significant effect on the atmospheric temperature. The layer extends from 80 km to 500 km above the Earth, with the air pressure equal to one-millionth that at ground level. During the daytime, the temperature of this layer can reach 1500°C due to the absorption of short-wavelength radiation. Ultraviolet radiation, X-rays and gamma-rays are all absorbed. The Aurora Borealis (or 'Northern Lights') and Aurora Australis (as seen in the Southern Hemisphere) occur at this level. The effect is caused by streams of charged particles from the Sun ionising the molecules in the atmosphere. The **ionosphere**, a region of ionised gas molecules, is part of the thermosphere.

● The **exosphere** – This is the uppermost layer, where the last atoms and molecules of the atmosphere are found.

The atmosphere is far from transparent, as the graph in Fig 5.8 shows. There are two effective windows, the **optical window** and the **radio window**. If we wish to make observations in the infrared, ultraviolet or X-ray regions, we need to use satellites or balloons.

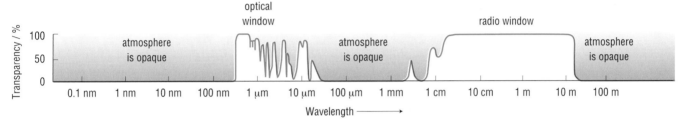

Fig 5.8 The atmosphere is opaque to many wavelengths of electromagnetic radiation.

QUESTION

5.5 Write down the approximate wavelength ranges of the two windows in the atmosphere.

The causes of absorption

The atmosphere is opaque to many regions of the electromagnetic spectrum. So what are the reasons for this opacity? Fig 5.9 shows a detailed picture of the transparency of the atmosphere in the ultraviolet, visible and infrared regions of the spectrum. The absorption of different wavelengths results from the presence of different types of molecules in the atmosphere. The most significant are:

oxygen O_2 water vapour H_2O
ozone O_3 carbon dioxide CO_2

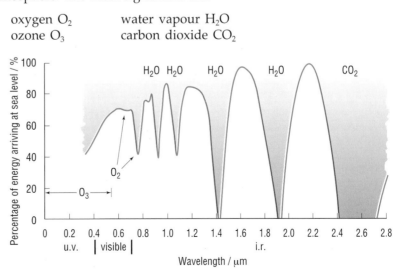

Fig 5.9 Molecular absorption means that the atmosphere is more transparent to some wavelengths than to others.

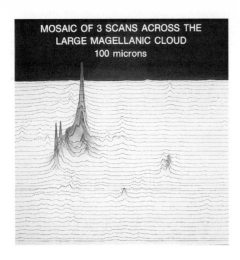

Fig 5.10 The Infra-Red Astronomical Satellite (IRAS) was used to produce this 'three-dimensional' scan. The tallest peak is emission from the Tarantula Nebula in the Large Magellanic Cloud.

When one of these molecules absorbs a photon of radiation, the vibrations of its constituent atoms increase. The photon must have a frequency that matches the vibrational frequency of the molecule; this is an example of **resonance**.

In the ultraviolet region, ozone is the main absorber. Ozone is formed by the action of sunlight on molecular oxygen. Therefore our observations need to be made from high-flying aircraft, balloons or satellites, the last of these providing the best results. The International Ultraviolet Explorer (IUE) satellite launched in 1978 has provided excellent observations in the far-ultraviolet, free from the cloaking effect of the Earth's atmosphere.

Radiation in the near-ultraviolet, the region just outside the visible spectrum, can penetrate the atmosphere. However, conventional glass is opaque to ultraviolet radiation, so refracting telescopes are of limited use. The IUE contains a Cassegrain reflecting telescope.

Moving to the infrared region, molecular oxygen is a problem. However, the effect is reduced if observatories are built at high altitudes (4000–5000 m), which is not unusual to avoid refraction problems from a turbulent atmosphere and the likelihood of clouds. There is an infrared telescope on the summit of Mauna Kea in Hawaii. Resonant effects of water vapour and carbon dioxide pose more problems at longer wavelengths, so satellites are used for the best observations. One example that has proved very effective is the Infra-Red Astronomical Satellite (IRAS), which was launched by NASA in 1983 – see Fig 5.10.

Scattering of light

Dust can also absorb and scatter light. The skies around the Earth can be affected by major volcanic eruptions such as Mount St Helens. In fact, there is evidence that poor summers and harsher-than-normal winters follow such events.

Large particles (those whose size is large relative to the wavelength of incident radiation) reflect light rather like mirrors. They do not change the colour of the light as it is scattered. An example of these are water droplets in clouds. Typically, water droplets are around 10 μm in size. They scatter all wavelengths equally, and hence the clouds appear white.

For particles whose size is much smaller than the wavelength of light, the scattering is greater for shorter wavelengths. (It has been shown to be proportional to $1/\lambda^4$.) Consequently, blue light is scattered about ten times as strongly as red light. This is known as **Rayleigh scattering**. Oxygen and nitrogen molecules in the air have a size around 0.5 nm, and cause this form of scattering.

This explains why we see a blue sky: the blue light that we receive from the Sun is strongly scattered as it passes through the atmosphere, and reaches our eyes from all directions. The red light is scattered less. This is why, when the Sun is close to the horizon, it appears red or orange. Most of the blue light in its spectrum has been scattered away.

Light pollution

Light pollution is a major problem for astronomers, as readers in major cities will be aware – see Fig 5.11. Street-lighting is rarely shielded, so that stray light makes it difficult to see any but the brightest stars at night. The Royal Greenwich Observatory was originally built in central London in 1675; however, the effect of pollution, smoke and electric lighting eventually made meaningful observation impossible. In 1967 the observatory was transferred to the Sussex village of Herstmonceux to overcome these problems. However, the British weather is not ideal, and as a consequence the decision was made to develop a branch of the Royal Greenwich

Fig 5.11 The glow from different types of street-lights in several small towns and villages, viewed through fog. Even on a clear night, light pollution makes astronomical observations difficult.

Observatory on La Palma in the Canary Islands, now the home of the Isaac Newton Telescope.

Ultimately the best solution for clear observations is to site a telescope in Earth orbit. The Hubble Space Telescope (HST) was placed in orbit in 1990. Initially there were problems with chromatic aberration (not by leaving the lens cap on, as was unkindly suggested by the press), which have now been rectified by astronauts. The effectiveness of this telescope can be judged by comparing the photographs in Fig 5.12.

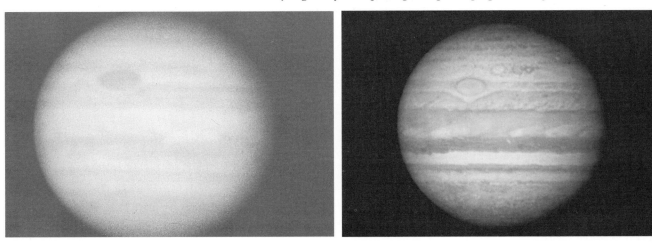

(a)   (b)

Fig 5.12 Two views of Jupiter, photographed (a) using an Earth-based telescope and (b) by the Hubble Space Telescope.

QUESTIONS	**5.6** Explain why there is no need to launch telescopes for radio astronomy into space.
	5.7 Why is it fortunate for all living creatures (not just astronomers) that the atmosphere is transparent to wavelengths in the visible region of the spectrum?
	5.8 Suggest how street-lights might be redesigned to minimise the amount of light pollution they produce.

Wave phenomena

Having considered the effect of the atmosphere on the light from stars, we will now go on to think about what happens when the light reaches an optical instrument – a telescope, or an eye. Now we have to take account of the effects of diffraction and interference, two phenomena that you should have come across, which are a consequence of the wave-like nature of light. We will start with a brief description of these two phenomena, concentrating on light passing through a single slit. (This is important in astronomy, because the light that enters a telescope is effectively passing through a gap, the circular end of the telescope.)

When light passes through a gap, **diffraction** may be observed. The light spreads out around the edges of the gap. This is shown for a single slit in Fig 5.13. The effect is greatest when the width of the gap is similar to the wavelength of the light.

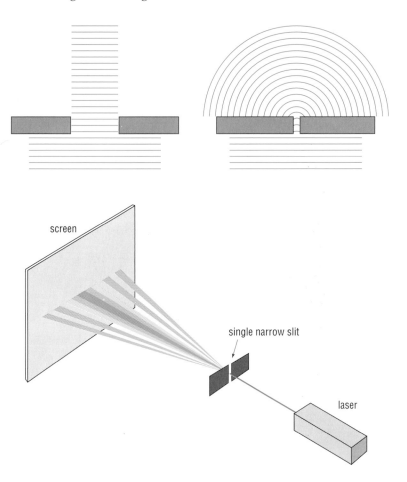

Fig 5.13 Diffraction of plane wavefronts by a single slit.

Fig 5.14 Experimental arrangement for viewing diffraction of light by a single slit.

When the diffracted light reaches a screen beyond the slit, a pattern of light and dark fringes may be seen. This is caused by **interference**. Waves from all points across the slit arrive at each point on the screen, and these interfere with each other. Where they interfere constructively, we see a light fringe. Destructive interference gives a dark fringe.

Fig 5.14 shows an experimental arrangement for demonstrating the diffraction of light by a single slit. Fig 5.15(a) shows the resulting pattern of fringes, which is known as a **Fraunhofer diffraction pattern**, and the graph of Fig 5.15(b) shows the variation in intensity across the screen. Notice that the central bright fringe has twice the width of the other fringes.

The minima in this pattern are numbered $n = 1, 2, 3$, etc., and $n = -1, -2, -3$, etc., as shown on the graph. They are referred to as the first-, second-

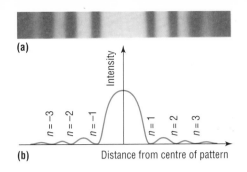

(a)

(b)

Fig 5.15 (a) The diffraction pattern for a single slit; (b) the variation of intensity across the pattern.

and third-order minima. Their positions are given by the following equation:

$$n\lambda = d \sin \theta$$

where n is the order of the minimum, λ is the wavelength of the light, d is the slit width, and θ is the angle at which the minimum appears. (Take care! This equation is very similar to that for diffraction by a grating, but in that case the equation gives the positions of the bright fringes, i.e. maxima.)

So, for red laser light of wavelength 648 nm passing through a slit of width 0.01 mm, the first-order minimum ($n = 1$) occurs at an angle θ given by

$$1 \times 648 \times 10^{-9} = 0.01 \times 10^{-3} \sin \theta$$

$$\sin \theta = \frac{648 \times 10^{-9}}{0.01 \times 10^{-3}} = 0.0648$$

$$\theta = 0.065 \text{ rad} = 3.7°$$

QUESTIONS

5.9 Orange light of wavelength 589 nm is diffracted as it passes through a narrow slit. The light falls on a screen 1 m from the slit. The two first-order minima are found to be separated by 10 cm on the screen. Calculate:
   (a) the angle θ that the first-order minimum makes with the straight-through direction;
   (b) the width of the slit.

   [Take care! Start by working out the distance of the first-order minimum from the centre of the central bright fringe.]

5.10 Will the two second-order minima in the diffraction pattern in question 5.9 be 20 cm apart? Check your answer with a calculation.

Circular apertures

Fraunhofer diffraction also occurs at circular openings. This is important for our consideration of optical instruments, because the eye and the telescope lens are both examples of circular apertures. The diffraction pattern formed is a series of concentric circular fringes – see Fig 5.16. (The central bright fringe is known as the **Airy disc**.)

Now, when light from a star enters a telescope, just such a diffraction pattern will be formed. Normally this is not important; however, when we are trying to look at two stars that are close together in our field of view, it can be very significant.

Suppose we are looking at two stars that appear side-by-side. If we cannot resolve them, they will appear to us as a single point of light. If they are further apart, we may be able to see them as two distinct points of light. What are the conditions for this to be the case?

 circular aperture

 central bright spot

Fig 5.16 The diffraction pattern that results when light is diffracted by a circular aperture.

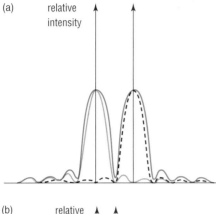

(a)

relative
intensity

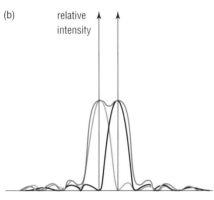

(b)

relative
intensity

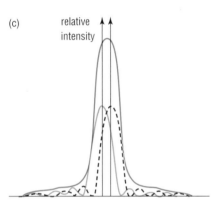

(c)

relative
intensity

Fig 5.17 Two light sources can only be resolved if their diffraction patterns do not overlap too closely: **(a)** well resolved; **(b)** just resolved; **(c)** not resolved.

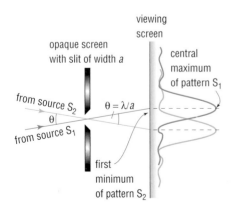

Fig 5.18 Rayleigh's criterion: if the two sources are to be just resolved, the central maximum of the diffraction pattern of one must coincide with the first minimum of the diffraction pattern of the other.

Fig 5.17 shows the result of two overlapping diffraction patterns, one from each star. In Fig 5.17(a), there are two clearly separated peaks, and the observer sees two stars. In Fig 5.17(c), there is only a single bright peak. The two stars are too close together for the observer to be able to resolve them. In Fig 5.17(b), there is a small dip in the diffraction pattern, and the observer could probably resolve the stars.

This middle picture is somewhat arbitrary. Rayleigh set down a well defined condition to determine unambiguously whether two sources of light could be resolved. He said that, if the two sources were to be just resolvable, they must be so far apart that the central bright fringe of one coincides with the first dark fringe of the other. This is shown in Fig 5.18 and is known as the **Rayleigh criterion**.

Rayleigh went on to show that, for this to be the case, the angular separation θ of the two sources of light must be at least

$$\theta = \frac{\lambda}{D}$$

where D is the diameter of the aperture through which the sources are being observed.

This gives us a measure of the resolving power of a telescope. As light enters the circular aperture at the front of the telescope, it is diffracted, and this limits the resolution that can be achieved. Note that, for improved resolving power, we require a large diameter and a short wavelength.

A typical amateur reflecting telescope might have an open end of diameter 15 cm. If we take the average wavelength of visible light to be 600 nm, we find that the resolving power can be no greater than

$$\theta = \frac{600 \, \text{nm}}{15 \, \text{cm}} = \frac{600 \times 10^{-9}}{0.15} = 4 \times 10^{-6} \, \text{rad}$$

Comparing resolving powers

Compare the resolving power of the telescope in the calculation above with the resolving power of the eye, which is about 3×10^{-4} rad. Clearly, the telescope can provide much greater resolution.

However, we must recall that the atmosphere itself limits resolution, and sets an upper limit of about 3×10^{-5} rad (see question 5.4 above). Hence the telescope's resolving power is better than it needs to be!

In practice, telescopes are made with large objectives because this helps them to gather light, and so their images are bright. Their resolving power is less than that suggested by the Rayleigh criterion, because it is limited by the effects of the atmosphere.

Finally, we must bear in mind the resolution achieved by the final detector – photographic film, CCD or the retina of the eye. In a good telescope, each star will appear as a tiny point of light. The detector must be able to resolve these points. It would be no good using photographic film whose grain size is large compared with the size of the tiny spot in the image which represents a single star. (This aspect of the sensitivity of detectors was dealt with in Chapter 4.)

A LIMITED VIEW

5.11 Use the Rayleigh criterion to estimate the resolving power of the eye.
[typical wavelength of visible light = 600 nm; diameter of pupil = 3 mm]

5.12 Radio waves are not seriously affected by the atmosphere, so the resolving power of a radio telescope is limited by diffraction effects. Calculate the resolving power of a radio telescope of diameter 50 m, for radio waves of wavelength 1 m.

5.4 RADIO ASTRONOMY

Radio telescopes

The radio telescopes of today are direct descendants of the primitive radio telescope built by Karl Jansky of Bell Laboratories in 1932. Jansky built his 'telescope', which was a set of radio antennae, so as to investigate the static that affects short-wavelength radio-telephone communication. The more conventional 'radio dish' was first built by Grote Reber, in Illinois, in 1936. This was the first instrument designed to map radio emission from the sky. The dish had a diameter of 9.1 m. Jodrell Bank in Cheshire (see Fig 5.19) is part of Manchester University and is typical of many radio telescopes, although the design may vary with the range of wavelengths that a telescope is designed to detect.

Fig 5.19 The famous radio telescope at Jodrell Bank.

We will now look at the factors that determine how a radio telescope is designed.

Shape and size

As with an optical reflector telescope, a parabolic reflector is used – see Fig 5.20. However, as the 250 ft (76 m) dish at Jodrell Bank shows, the scale is totally different. Radio waves typically have wavelengths a million

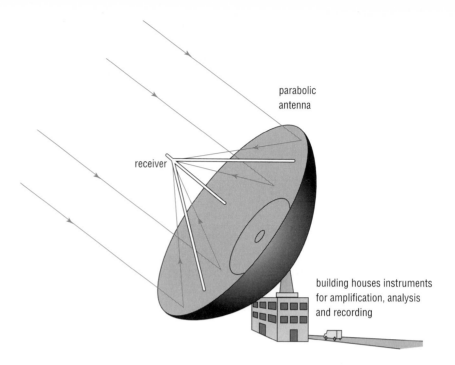

parabolic
antenna

receiver

building houses instruments
for amplification, analysis
and recording

Fig 5.20 The construction of a radio telescope
dish and detector system.

times greater than those of visible light, so the size and the absolute
smoothness of the reflecting surface are not as crucial as for light. Indeed,
wire mesh can be used as an alternative to metal sheeting, as long as the
mesh size is less than 1/20th of a wavelength, whilst the surface does not
need to be polished.

The 'gathering power' of the radio telescope is improved with greater
size just as with an optical telescope. In fact, the power is proportional to
the area of the telescope, and hence to the square of the diameter:

gathering power $\propto$ diameter^2

Resolving power

With such large sizes you might think that radio telescopes would produce
detailed images. However, this is not the case, since the resolving power
is linked to the wavelength of radiation being studied. In section 5.3 we
found

$$\theta = \frac{\lambda}{D}$$

where θ was the angular separation and D the diameter of the reflector.
Radio waves have long wavelengths, and so the angular resolution is poor.

QUESTIONS

5.13 Calculate the resolving power of the Jodrell Bank radio telescope
(diameter 76 m) for radio waves of wavelength 1 m. How does
your answer compare with the resolving power of the human
eye?

5.14 Use your knowledge of diffraction to explain why the reflecting
surface of a radio telescope can be made from wire mesh, rather
than from solid metal.

5.15 It has been said that a 5 m optical telescope can resolve a
10 pence piece at a distance of 10 miles. A similar-sized radio
telescope could not resolve the same coin if it were held a few
metres in front of it. Are these statements true? Do some
calculations to show how you reached your answer.

Convection currents in the atmosphere do not affect radio observations, so the telescope's resolving power is limited by the diameter of the telescope. In addition, radio telescopes have the obvious advantage that observations can be made at any time of the day or night.

Looking around

The parabolic dish itself is not a detector but simply a radiation-gathering surface. Radio waves from space are focused by the dish onto a detector (a small aerial) at its focus. The signal is weak, and must be amplified at a pre-amplifier, and taken by wire to a control room. At the control room the signal is further amplified, for a high gain, using a low-noise amplifier to ensure that as little noise as possible is added to the signal.

Now the required radio frequency is chosen by means of a tuner. Most modern radio telescopes can receive radiation of different wavelengths simultaneously, and then separate the signals for independent analysis. This increases the efficiency of the telescope. The information gained is then stored on computer.

This process gives a single measurement for the intensity of the radio waves being received from a particular direction in space. To build up a complete picture of a region of the sky, the telescope must be scanned from side to side and up and down.

The largest radio telescope is the Arecibo dish (Fig 5.21), with a diameter of 300 m (1000 ft), which is built in a natural, roughly parabolic, valley in Puerto Rico. The antenna is suspended above the dish. The large size gives improved resolution; however, the telescope lacks manoeuvrability. The telescope sweeps across the sky as a result of the Earth's rotation.

Fig 5.21   The radio telescope at Arecibo, Puerto Rico, is built into a natural dish-shaped valley.

The radio Universe

The information gained from radio telescopes can be used to investigate many things. These include analysing chemical elements in stars and the motion of the planets (using the Doppler effect – see section 7.5). At shorter wavelengths, in the microwave region, evidence of the Big Bang can be investigated. Quasars and pulsars owed their discovery to radio astronomy.

Since radio waves can penetrate dust in space, they can be used to look into the centre of our galaxy, the Milky Way. Such a view is shown in Fig 5.22. We are unable to see the nucleus of our galaxy with visible light, because of the dust that blocks our view.

As Fig 5.8 showed, not all radio wavelengths are available for investigation. At the microwave end, water vapour and carbon dioxide block out radiation with a wavelength less than 1 cm. At longer wavelengths (above 20 m) radio waves are absorbed by the atmosphere.

For those wavelengths that can pass through the atmosphere, 'radio pollution' poses the biggest problem. Just as optical telescopes suffer from light pollution, radio signals generated on Earth can interfere with signals from space. At all radio frequencies, radio broadcasts are a problem. Specific problems include radio-telephones and radio-pagers, which operate in the 100–1000 MHz range, and radar, in the 400–10 000 MHz range. Orbiting satellites used for navigation and broadcasting pose a further problem, as they pass in the 'field of view' of radio telescopes. This is why the licensing of new satellite television stations is strictly controlled.

Recently there has been a trend to site new radio telescopes away from centres of population. Microwave observatories are often on top of mountains.

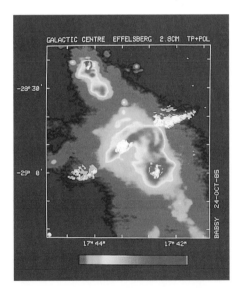

Fig 5.22   A radio telescope view of the centre of our galaxy, the Milky Way.

Radio interferometry

The problem of resolving power becomes acute for long-wavelength radio waves. A clever technique has been developed to overcome this. Radio signals can be carried by electrical wires; this enables radio telescopes many kilometres apart to be linked together. A good example is the Very Large Array (VLA), in New Mexico, USA (Fig 5.23). This consists of 27 parabolic radio dishes arranged in a Y configuration over an area with a diameter of 27 km. Each dish has a diameter of 26 m.

Fig 5.23 The Very Large Array (VLA) in New Mexico, USA, is a radio interferometer.

This arrangement is called a **radio interferometer**, as the signals from the dishes are made to interfere with one another. Signals arriving from a distant region of space arrive at the dishes at different times. By matching up these signals, any noise in an individual signal can be eliminated. This produces a sharp and clear signal despite the initial weakness of the signal due to the 'incompleteness' of the dish. An added advantage is that electrical noise can be filtered out, as it will be different for each dish.

Theoretically it is possible to put two telescopes on opposite sides of the Earth, to produce an extreme example of very-long-baseline interferometry (VLBI). This would produce a resolution of 0.016 arcsec (seconds of arc), still only just comparable with the best optical telescopes.

QUESTION	**5.16** The atmosphere is opaque to radio waves with a wavelength above 20 m. Scientists might construct a suitable radio telescope that could be placed in Earth orbit. How big would such a telescope have to be to give reasonable resolving power? What problems might there be for such an exercise?

5.5 FUTURE ASTRONOMY

X-ray and gamma-ray astronomy

Neither X-rays nor gamma-rays can penetrate the atmosphere, so until recently this has been a branch of astronomy where little was known. However, several satellites in the 1970s opened up the field of X-ray

A LIMITED VIEW

astronomy. X-rays are produced by violent, high-energy events. In particular, matter falling into a black hole will emit X-rays. This is discussed later in section 9.4. The satellite Uhuru (Swahili for 'freedom'), launched in 1970, detected over 170 X-ray sources. More recently, in the 1980s, there were ROSAT, Exosat and Einstein. NASA have a major satellite planned for the late 1990s. This is AXAF (the Advanced X-ray Astrophysics Facility), which will have a 1.2 m telescope operating at wavelengths in the range 0.15 nm to 6 nm.

Gamma-rays are produced by the hottest and most violent objects in the Universe. Gamma-ray astronomy is still in its infancy, as these rays are impossible to focus and difficult to detect. Nevertheless gamma-ray telescopes have been launched by both the USA and Russia. The 17 tonne Gamma Ray Observatory, which was launched by NASA in 1991, is designed to map the whole sky.

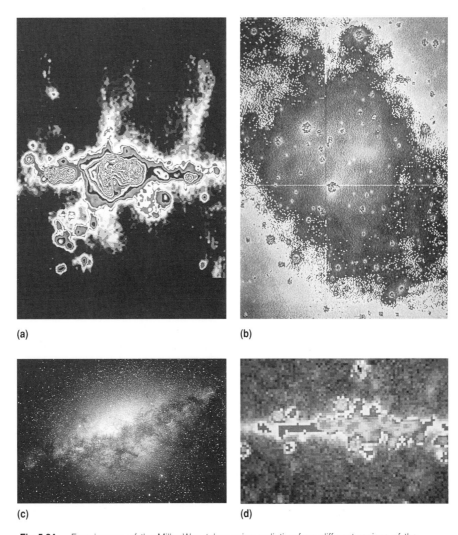

(a) (b)

(c) (d)

Fig 5.24 Four images of the Milky Way, taken using radiation from different regions of the electromagnetic spectrum: **(a)** radio, **(b)** infrared, **(c)** visible and **(d)** X-ray.

QUESTION	5.17 Fig 5.24 shows the Milky Way photographed at wavelengths in four different regions of the electromagnetic spectrum: radio, infrared, visible and X-rays. Comment on the different aspects of the galaxy that each photograph could show up.

A LIMITED VIEW   71

The economics of astronomy

People have always endeavoured to find out more about their surroundings, from ancient times to the present day. Nevertheless financial considerations are becoming more important. The 'space race' of the 1960s was fuelled by political ambition, the Russians gaining *kudos* with the launch of Sputnik 1 in 1957, and with Yuri Gagarin becoming the first man in space in 1961. The Americans gained the accolade of placing the first men on the Moon in 1969.

All of these were expensive projects, as were the orbiting space laboratories. Once the Moon landing had occurred, one of the greatest goals had been achieved. By the time of the ill-fated Apollo 13 mission, interest had waned. It was the human interest story that gave the Apollo programme further publicity. Despite this, the Apollo programme was cut short for financial reasons. Apollo 13 and the 'Challenger' Space Shuttle accident also reminded us of the dangers of manned space-flight.

The Space Shuttle programme was developed at a high cost, as it enabled the spacecraft to be re-used. Nevertheless its success has relied upon commercial usage, such as placing communication, weather and military satellites into orbit.

The Hubble Space Telescope was put into orbit in 1990 at a cost of $1.2 billion, with a further $630 million being spent in 1993 to correct its faults. On the ground, the European Southern Observatory is planning a £225 million 16 m telescope, in the Atacama Desert in Chile. The observatory should be functional in 1998.

Can we justify such expenditure? Weather and telecommunication satellites may have economic pay-offs, but pure astronomical research has not. Both the USA and Russia have reduced their scientific budgets. Russia had diverted much-needed funds into the space and military programmes at a cost to its people, as has become apparent with the dissolution of the old Soviet Union. The USA is not without its problems, with many areas of urban deprivation, and at the time of writing (Spring 1996) severe problems with its local government expenditure.

Would this money be better put into giving aid to 'Third World' countries, to help them develop? How important is it to find out more about astronomy and our place in the Universe, when there are major social and environmental problems in the world?

ASSIGNMENT

The cost of the Hubble Space Telescope and the European Southern Observatory appear large by our everyday standards. They might be put into perspective if we compare them with other expenditure. Listed below are some recent annual budgets from the USA and the UK.

US annual Government budget: $1600 000 million

Share for:	Defence	17%
	Education	14%
	Health	12%

UK annual Government budget: $280 000 million

Share for:	Defence	11%
	Education	12%
	Health	12%

Use these figures and other information you can find to write an essay on the economic considerations involved in spending money on astronomical research. Try to justify any decisions and opinions you express.

A LIMITED VIEW

SUMMARY

Observations in the optical (visible) region are hampered by absorption, scattering and refraction in the atmosphere.

Infrared, ultraviolet, X-ray and gamma-ray astronomy can only be successfully studied by detectors placed above the atmosphere.

Radio telescopes usually consist of large parabolic dishes that focus the radio waves onto a detector.

The resolving power of radio telescopes is poor; this has led to the development of large interferometer arrays.

Astronomical research that involves major observatories and satellite detectors is expensive. Its value has to be weighed up against competing priorities in national budgets.

Chapter 6

INTERPRETING LIGHT FROM THE STARS

The previous two chapters described how observations may be made using visible light or other types of electromagnetic radiation. Observations are made so that we can find out more about the Universe and the objects in it. Despite the immense distances to the stars, we can find out a great deal. As far as we can tell, the laws of physics are no different in other parts of the Universe, so it is possible to deduce the surface temperature, chemical composition, mass and distance of stars and other astronomical objects. This chapter concentrates on the techniques employed in finding out this information.

LEARNING OBJECTIVES

After studying this chapter you should be able to:

1. explain what is meant by black-body radiation, and how this accounts for the colour of stars;

2. understand what is meant by luminosity and flux;

3. explain how spectroscopy is used in astrophysics;

4. classify stars in terms of their luminosity, temperature and colour.

6.1 THE SURFACE TEMPERATURE OF STARS

Black-body radiation

You will be familiar with the terms 'red hot' and 'white hot'; hot objects glow, and the hotter they are, the brighter and whiter is the light they give out. We can use this idea to find out about the temperature of stars by looking at their colours.

You are probably also familiar with the idea of thermal imaging – Fig 6.1. This can be used for searching for buried victims in an earthquake or by the military forces to gain night-time vision. So what is thermal radiation?

Thermal radiation is energy that travels as electromagnetic waves. It is radiated by all objects – even cold objects produce some thermal radiation in the infrared region of the spectrum, but hotter objects produce more, and at higher frequencies. When the temperature of a hot object approaches 1000°C, some of its thermal radiation will be in the visible region of the spectrum.

To see how the appearance of an object depends on its temperature, we will introduce the idea of a 'black body'. A **black body** is a perfect absorber, an object that absorbs all the radiation of every wavelength falling on it. At room temperature it will appear black, since it does not reflect light.

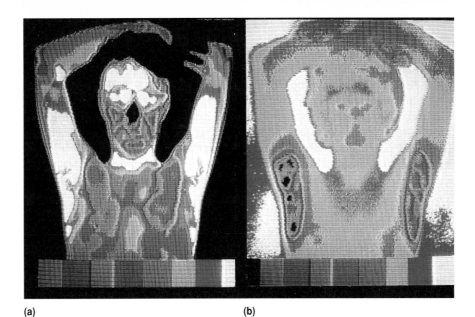

Fig 6.1 The human body emits infrared radiation. This pair of thermograms shows a man holding his arms above his head in (**a**) cold conditions and (**b**) warm conditions

(a)   **(b)**

However, good absorbers are also good emitters. Therefore, it follows that, at any given temperature, a black body must be a perfect emitter of radiation. So, at high temperatures, it will emit radiation including visible light, and its appearance is then *anything but* black!

In practice, most objects with which we are familiar in everyday life are not perfect emitters of radiation. However, for stars, this is a good first approximation, which we can use to help us to find out their temperatures.

Black-body spectrum

Fig 6.2 shows the spectrum of radiation that has been measured for black bodies. This shows the following points:

- A hot object emits radiation across a broad range of wavelengths.
- There is a peak in intensity at a particular wavelength.
- The hotter the object, the higher the peak.
- The hotter the object, the shorter the peak wavelength.

(Note that the area under the graph is the total energy radiated per unit time per unit surface area at a given temperature.)

Let's look at the curve for a black body at a temperature of 1400 K (about 1100°C). The peak wavelength is at approximately 2 μm. This is in the infrared region of the spectrum. However, the shortest wavelengths of the radiation produced are in the visible region, and so an object at this temperature is hot enough to emit light – it glows. Most of the radiation it emits is in the infrared – think about what you notice if you stand close to a bonfire for any length of time.

QUESTION

6.1 Look carefully at the graph of Fig 6.2.

    (a) How can you tell that a black body at 1400 K emits more radiation than a body at 1200 K?

    (b) Why is a black body at 1000 K likely to look black?

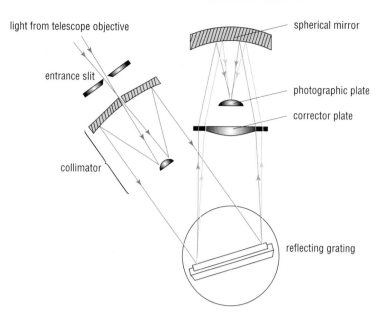

Fig 6.5 Astronomical spectrometers generally use reflecting diffraction gratings. This is a spectrograph, which produces a photographic image of a star's spectrum.

Two types of grating are used. With a transmission grating, which most readers will have seen in a school laboratory, light passes through the grating. With a reflecting grating, light is reflected from the grating. The latter is the preferred arrangement for astronomical use. Fig 6.5 shows a typical arrangement.

INVESTIGATION

Use a spectrometer with a diffraction grating to look at the spectra of some lamps in the laboratory (see Fig 6.6). You might look at:

- sodium, hydrogen, helium and mercury lamps;
- a tungsten filament lamp.

If you can measure the angles at which particular colours appear in the spectrum, you will be able to work out their wavelengths.

[Detailed experimental arrangements and how to calculate wavelengths will be found in standard A-level physics texts.]

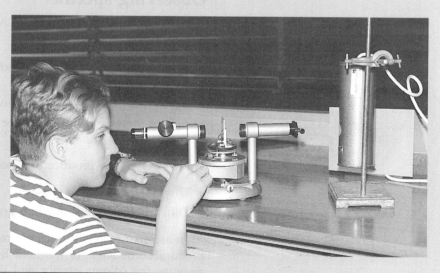

Fig 6.6 Measuring wavelengths using a laboratory spectrometer.

INTERPRETING LIGHT FROM THE STARS

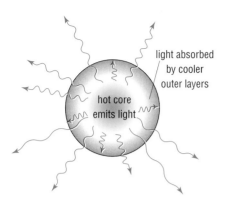

Fig 6.7 Atoms at the surface of a star absorb some of the light coming from within the star.

Emission and absorption spectra

Stars emit light when their atoms or molecules lose energy. This can happen when an electron drops to a lower energy level in an atom, or when a molecule vibrates less. Investigating the spectrum of light from a star can tell us about the atoms and molecules from which it is made.

We have already considered the spectrum of a black body. (This is represented in Fig 6.2.) This is known as a **continuous spectrum** because all wavelengths in a wide range are present.

A hot body may also produce a **line spectrum**. This consists of a number of bright lines at particular wavelengths. You can see such lines in the spectrum shown in Fig 6.8(a). These lines are due to electrons dropping from higher energy levels to lower energy levels. Since atoms of different elements have different energy levels, it follows that the wavelengths present in a line spectrum are characteristic of the elements present in the star. Consequently a line spectrum is a fingerprint of the energy changes within the atom, with different elements having different fingerprints.

The spectra described above are both classified as **emission spectra**, because they arise from light emitted by atoms and molecules in a star. However, when starlight is examined, a second type of line spectrum may be observed. Rather than bright lines being seen in the spectrum, dark lines are seen crossing the continuous background. This is an **absorption spectrum**.

Fig 6.7 shows how this can arise. The inside of a star is hot (much hotter than the surface). Light from the inside must pass through the outer layers before it can escape into space. Some of the light is absorbed by atoms in the outer layers; the wavelengths absorbed are characteristic of the atoms present.

Fig 6.8 shows the emission and absorption spectra for helium. You can see that the absorption lines in the absorption spectrum appear at the same wavelengths as the emission lines. Hence the absorption spectrum can also be used to identify the elements present in a star.

Absorption lines are sometimes known as Fraunhofer lines. They are named after the German scientist Joseph von Fraunhofer who, in 1814, first discovered dark lines crossing the Sun's spectrum. Interestingly, helium was first detected in the Sun before it was discovered on the Earth, hence its name, the Greek word for Sun being *helios*.

(a)

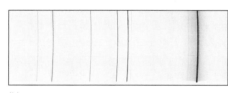

(b)

Fig 6.8 **(a)** The emission spectrum of helium shows emission lines. **(b)** The absorption spectrum of helium shows absorption lines at the same wavelengths.

Measuring intensity

Astronomers don't just measure the wavelengths of light present in a star's spectrum; they also obtain useful information from measurements of the **intensity** of each wavelength. Plots of intensity against wavelength for emission and absorption spectra have the general form shown in Fig 6.9.

Spectroscopy is discussed in further detail in the chapters on stellar evolution and cosmology in Theme 3. Note that spectroscopy can be carried out with radiation other than visible light; the infrared and ultraviolet regions produce a great deal of information.

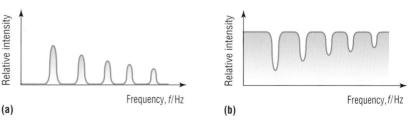

Fig 6.9 Intensity–wavelength graphs for line spectra: **(a)** emission and **(b)** absorption.

6.9 Line spectra arise in situations where atoms are 'isolated'; that is, they are well separated from their nearest neighbours. Continuous spectra arise in situations where atoms are close together, and where collisions between atoms occur very frequently. Suggest which type of emission spectrum you would expect to observe for the following sources:
(a) hot, low-pressure helium gas;
(b) a tungsten filament lamp.

[If you have carried out the investigation earlier in this section, you will know what type of spectrum each of these produces.]

6.10 The spectrum of a star typically has three components:

a continuous (black-body) background,
emission lines,
absorption lines.

Sketch a graph of intensity against wavelength to represent this. Label the three components in your sketch.

[Hint: Combine the graphs shown in Figs 6.2 and 6.9.]

6.5 THE SPECTRAL CLASSIFICATION OF STARS

Spectra and temperature

When astronomers look at the spectra of stars, they see differences between them. An understanding of the origins of spectra can help to explain these differences. Note that stellar spectra show that stars are similar to each other in terms of chemical composition. The differences in spectra arise largely because of differences in the temperatures of the stars.

So how does a star's spectrum depend on its temperature?

One feature that astronomers look for is the **Balmer series** of spectral lines. These arise from electrons in hydrogen atoms. When an electron drops from a high energy level to the second ($n = 2$) level, it emits light whose wavelength is in the visible region of the spectrum. Some of the possible transitions are shown in Fig 6.10, together with the wavelengths to which they give rise. The intensity of these Balmer lines in a star's spectrum can give us a clue to the star's temperature.

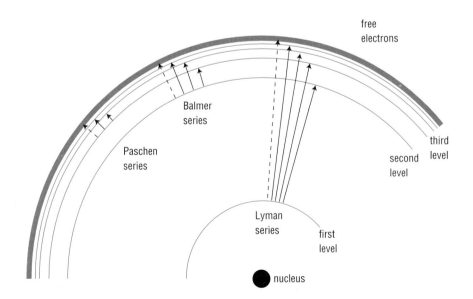

Fig 6.10 Energy levels of the hydrogen atom, and electron transitions that give rise to the Balmer series of lines.

In a cool star (surface temperature 4000 K), there are very few violent collisions between atoms to excite the electrons. Consequently, most electrons are in their lowest energy level (their ground state) and they change levels relatively rarely. The spectrum contains only weak absorption lines. In particular, the Balmer lines are weak.

In a hot star (surface temperature 20 000 K), there are many violent collisions between atoms. Electrons are in higher levels ($n = 3, 4$, etc.), with comparatively few in the second level. Hence few electrons are available to absorb wavelengths in the Balmer series, and again only weak absorption lines are observed.

For a star at an intermediate temperature (e.g. 10 000 K), many electrons are in the second energy level ($n = 2$) and are available to absorb the appropriate wavelengths of light. So the spectrum of this star shows strong Balmer absorption lines.

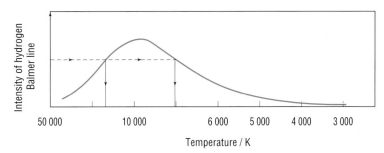

Fig 6.11 The strength of the Balmer absorption lines depends on a star's surface temperature. (Note that the temperature scale increases from right to left in this diagram.)

Fig 6.11 summarises this. The intensity of Balmer absorption lines is greatest at a temperature of approximately 10 000 K. Measuring their intensity gives an indication of the star's temperature.

You will notice from Fig 6.11 that this result is ambiguous. For a particular intensity, two temperatures are possible. This problem can be solved by looking at an element other than hydrogen. The peak absorption for different elements occurs at different temperatures, as shown in Fig 6.12. By comparing the absorption intensities of different elements, an unambiguous value for the star's temperature can be deduced.

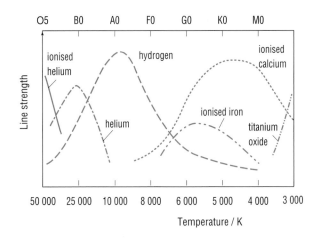

Fig 6.12 The strength of spectral lines due to different elements depends on a star's surface temperature.

QUESTION

6.11 Use the information in Fig 6.12 to suggest which elements would show up prominently in the spectra of the following stars:
(a) our Sun (a yellow star, surface temperature 5800 K);
(b) Betelgeuse (a red supergiant, surface temperature 3000 K);
(c) Rigel (a blue giant, surface temperature 14 000 K).

Atoms and molecules

In practice, there are other clues in the spectrum of a star that can help us to deduce its temperature.

Very hot stars show intense absorption lines for lighter elements; cooler stars have intense absorption lines for heavier elements. You can see this pattern in the graph of Fig 6.12. In particular, you will notice that helium absorption lines are only seen in the hottest stars. (The reason for this distinction is beyond the scope of this book.)

Cool stars also show spectral lines that arise from the presence of small molecules in their atmospheres. At high temperatures, molecules cannot survive the energetic collisions which are occurring all the time. Lower temperatures are needed if molecules are to survive. ('Lower', of course, means a few thousand kelvins!)

Spectral classes

Stars with similar spectra can be grouped together. This was first done by the American physicist Annie J. Cannon in the 1890s. She classified thousands of stars into alphabetical classes A to Q. Since then, some of the classes have been merged, regrouped or dropped, leaving us with the seven classes shown in Table 6.1.

Table 6.1 Spectral classes of stars and characteristics of their spectra

Spectral class	Approximate surface temperature/K	Hydrogen Balmer lines	Other spectral features
O	40 000	weak	ionised helium
B	20 000	medium	neutral helium
A	10 000	strong	weak ionised calcium
F	7 500	medium	weak ionised calcium
G	5 500	weak	medium ionised calcium
K	4 500	very weak	strong ionised calcium
M	3 000	very weak	strong titanium oxide

These spectral classes have been subdivided, so that class A has subclasses A0–A9, and so on. This subdivision enables a star's temperature to be classified to within 5%. In this categorisation, our Sun is classified as a G2 star with a surface temperature of 5800 K.

In Chapter 8 we will see what this information on the temperature and composition of stars can tell us about the life history of stars.

QUESTIONS

6.12 Use Table 6.1 to predict two features you would expect to see in the spectrum of light from the Sun.
[surface temperature of Sun = 5800 K]

6.13 The photograph shown in Fig 6.13 dates from 1886. It shows the spectra of four well known stars. The lines at shorter wavelength (on the left) correspond to hydrogen and helium, whilst the lines at longer wavelength (to the right) correspond to calcium and titanium oxide.

Use Fig 6.12 and Table 6.1 to suggest the correct spectral class for each star.

Fig 6.13 Typical spectra of stars of different classes (see question 6.13). From the top the stars are the Sun, Sirius, Aldebaran and Betelgeuse.

6.14 The order of spectral classes can be remembered by the rather sexist mnemonic 'Oh Be A Fine Girl, Kiss Me'. The first letters of the words provide the required letters. Devise a more acceptable mnemonic for this. (Any suitable alternatives will be gratefully received by the author!)

SUMMARY

A black body is a perfect emitter and absorber of radiation, with a characteristic spectrum.

Wien's displacement law states that the maximum energy radiated by a black body is at a wavelength λ_{max} that depends on the body's absolute temperature:

$$\lambda_{max}T = 0.002\,89 \text{ m K}$$

Stefan's law can be used to estimate the power output of a star:

$$P = \sigma A T^4$$

where Stefan's constant $\sigma = 5.67 \times 10^{-8} \text{ W m}^{-2} \text{ K}^{-4}$.

The spectra of stars show a continuous background with absorption and emission lines characteristic of the elements present.

Spectra can be interpreted to give information about the star's temperature and composition.

Chapter 7

MEASURING ASTRONOMICAL DISTANCES

Looking at the night sky is a history lesson. We see the Moon as it was 1¼ seconds ago whilst light from the Sun takes over 8 minutes to reach us. And what about the stars? Light from the nearest star takes 4.3 years to reach us, whilst light from the most distant stellar and galactic objects can take millions or indeed billions of years!

In astronomy, distances can be very large indeed. Astronomers have developed a range of techniques for measuring these distances; estimating the distance to a distant galaxy requires a different technique to that used for finding the distance to the nearest stars. This chapter looks at these different techniques.

LEARNING OBJECTIVES

After studying this chapter you should be able to:

1. understand how parallax can be used to measure the distances to planets and stars;

2. understand the concepts of apparent and absolute magnitude;

3. appreciate the link between luminosity and magnitude;

4. understand how Cepheid variable stars are used to estimate large distances;

5. understand why the light of distant objects is red-shifted;

6. understand Hubble's law and use it to estimate the age of the Universe;

7. understand how the Doppler effect is used in determining the motion of stars and planets.

7.1 STELLAR DISTANCES

Using parallax

In Chapter 1 we saw how Kepler was able to use observations of the positions of the planets to deduce his three laws of planetary motion. These observations involved measuring the angular position of the planets in the night sky. He used trigonometry to deduce the shapes of their orbits.

Kepler's work was possible because the planets are relatively close to the Earth. Things are more complicated when we come to consider the stars. The stars are literally millions of times further away and we see them as mere pinpoints of light forming an apparently fixed pattern in the night sky. So just how far away are they?

Fig 7.1 Parallax: the apparent position of the church spire against the distant background of mountains depends on your viewpoint.

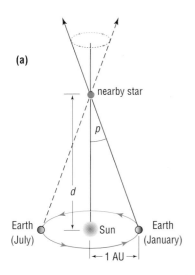

(a)

nearby star

p

d

Earth (July)

Sun

Earth (January)

← 1 AU →

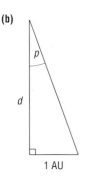

(b)

p

d

1 AU

Fig 7.2 The position of a star is measured against the background of distant stars at an interval of six months; this is used to find its parallax.

The simplest method of measuring the distance to the stars is by using **parallax**. Parallax is the apparent shifting of an object against a distant background when viewed from two different points, as illustrated in Fig 7.1. (You may like to try this: Close one eye, and raise a finger so as to hide someone nearby in your class from the viewpoint of your open eye. Now swap which eye is closed. The person comes back into view. Your two eyes have slightly different views of the world.)

The stars form a pattern in the sky, and our view of the pattern depends on where we view it from. We can use this to determine the position of a near star against the background of more distant stars. We need two viewpoints as far apart as possible if we are to see the greatest change in apparent position of a star relative to more distant stars. The longest baseline we can establish between two viewpoints is the opposite extremities of the Earth's orbit around the Sun, a distance of two astronomical units (2 AU).

Fig 7.2(a) shows the positions of the Earth at an interval of six months. Looking at a nearby star, an observer will see it at slightly different angles at these two times in the year. By measuring the parallax angle p, and knowing the diameter of the Earth's orbit, the distance d to the star can be calculated.

Two points to note about this diagram:

- The closeness of the star is greatly exaggerated; the nearest star to the Sun is at a distance greater than 200 000 AU. Consequently the angle to be measured is very small.

- If the star was at a *greater* distance, the parallax angle would be *smaller*. The distance has an inverse relationship to the parallax angle.

From the triangle shown in Fig 7.2(b), you can see that the relationship involves the tangent of the angle:

$$d = 1 \, \text{AU} / \tan p$$

A star whose parallax is one second of arc (1 arcsec) is said to be at a distance of 1 parsec (see section 1.5 and Fig 1.21):

$$\text{distance (in parsec, pc)} = \frac{1}{\text{parallax angle (in arcsec)}}$$

Remembering that there are 60 arcsec in 1 arcmin, and 60 arcmin in 1 degree, we can calculate the equivalent distance in AU:

$$1 \, \text{parsec} = \frac{1 \, \text{AU}}{\tan(1 \, \text{arcsec})} = \frac{1 \, \text{AU}}{\tan(1/3600)^{\circ}} = 2.06 \times 10^5 \, \text{AU}$$

This is the same as 3.08×10^{16} m or 3.26 ly (light-years).

Clearly, the nearer a star is, the easier it is to measure its parallax. By 1838, astronomical instruments were sufficiently precise for some very small angles to be measured. It was in this year that the German astronomer Friedrich Bessel measured the distance to a star known as 61 Cygni, which is barely visible to the naked eye. He measured a parallax angle of 0.3 arcsec. Therefore, the distance of 61 Cygni from Earth is $1/0.3 = 3.33$ pc (or 11 ly).

Parallax is useful for stars up to a distance of about 100 pc (326 ly) where the parallax angle is 0.01 arcsec. This is at the limit of reliability of ground-based equipment, owing to the extreme accuracy required in measuring such small angles. However, away from the ground, orbiting telescopes such as Hipparcos (launched by the European Space Agency in 1989) avoid the distortions of the atmosphere.

7.1 Table 7.1 shows the parallax angles measured for three stars.
(a) Which star is nearest?
(b) Which star is furthest?
(c) Calculate the distance to the nearest of these stars, in parsecs (pc), in light-years (ly) and in astronomical units (AU).

Table 7.1   Some stars and their parallax angles

Star	Parallax angle / arcsec
Sirius	0.37
Arcturus	0.09
Procyon	0.29

7.2 The nearest star to the Solar System is Alpha Centauri, which is at a distance of 4.3 light-years. Calculate the parallax angle that must be measured to determine this.

Proper motion

The most distant stars in our galaxy are so far away that we cannot possibly measure their parallax angles. They form an apparently fixed pattern, and it is against this pattern that the parallax of nearer stars is observed. The angles involved are far too small to be observed with the naked eye, so we assume that the pattern of stars in the sky remains effectively fixed.

However, there is a slow but steady drift of some stars across the sky. This was first noticed by Edmund Halley in 1718, when he was studying the ancient Greek star charts of Hipparchus. He noticed that the positions of three bright stars, Sirius, Procyon and Arcturus, had changed in the intervening centuries. This was the first proof that the stars are moving relative to one another. Modern measurements show these movements to be 1.324, 1.247 and 3.678 arcsec per year. This motion perpendicular to our line of sight is known as **proper motion**. For these three close stars the proper motion is ten times greater than their parallax movement, so care has to be exercised in calculating their distances.

The proper motion of stars has the effect of changing the shape of well known constellations. The effect on Ursa Major (the Great Bear or Big Dipper) is shown in Fig 7.3.

Modern measurements have shown that the Sun (and the whole Solar System) is moving at a speed of 19.5 km s^{-1} relative to nearby stars, while revolving around the galactic centre at a speed of 300 km s^{-1}.

(a)   100 000 years ago

(b)   Present

(c)   100 000 years in the future

Fig 7.3   The shape of constellations changes over the centuries owing to the proper motion of the stars.

7.2 SPECTROSCOPIC PARALLAX

Beyond 100 parsecs

As mentioned above, parallax measurements are not possible for stars beyond a distance of about 100 pc. Beyond this distance, a different technique must be used. This is **spectroscopic parallax**, which in fact has *nothing* to do with parallax, despite the name!

The principle is this: If all stars were equally bright, then we could deduce that the dimmer they appeared, the farther away they must be.

Of course, all stars are not equally bright; however, we can use our knowledge of the spectra of stars (Chapter 6) to work out how hot a star is, and hence how bright it actually is. Then, from its apparent brightness, and using the inverse square law, we can work out how far away it is.

We will look at this process in stages.

Apparent magnitudes

Stars were first classified by their brightness around 2000 years ago by the Greek astronomer Hipparchus. The brightest stars were assigned a magnitude of 1, whilst the dimmest seen by the naked eye had a magnitude of 6. Intermediate values were given to the stars whose brightnesses were in between. This is a very awkward scale, but it is still in general use. Since the scale is concerned with comparing how bright different stars *appear* to be, these magnitudes are called **apparent magnitudes**.

Magnitude 1 stars are now *defined* to be 100 times brighter than magnitude 6 stars. So how does a difference of one magnitude affect the light intensity?

From magnitude 6 to magnitude 1 is a change of 5 magnitudes, corresponding to a factor of 100 in brightness. So if a factor of x gives a change of 1 magnitude, it follows that $x \times x \times x \times x \times x = x^5$ gives a change of 5 magnitudes, and we can write

$$x^5 = 100$$

Hence

$$x = 100^{1/5}$$

So $x = 2.512$

[Check: $2.512^5 = 100$.] Therefore a magnitude 1 star is 2.512 times as bright as a magnitude 2 star – we receive approximately 2.5 times as much light from it per second. And a magnitude 2 star is 2.512 times as bright as a magnitude 3 star, and so on. A scale like this is called *logarithmic*; equal steps up the scale correspond to multiplying by a constant factor.

Negative magnitudes continue for increasing brightness. Sirius, the brightest star in the night sky, has an apparent magnitude of –1.46. We can even include the Sun on this scale: its apparent magnitude is –26.7. Fig 7.4 shows some typical apparent magnitudes. Note that the faintest object yet photographed has an apparent magnitude of 26.

Another way to represent the relationship between apparent brightness m of a star and the intensity I of its light reaching the Earth is through the logarithmic equation

$$m = -2.512 \log I + \text{constant}$$

Calculating brightness ratios

To calculate the ratio of brightnesses of two objects:

- Step 1   Calculate the difference in their magnitudes, n.
- Step 2   Calculate the ratio of their brightnesses = 2.512^n.

Worked example

The Sun (magnitude –26.7) is brighter than the full Moon (magnitude –12.7). How many times brighter is the Sun than the Moon?

- Step 1   Difference in magnitudes = $(-12.7) - (-26.7) = +14.0$
- Step 2   Ratio of brightnesses = $2.512^{14.0} = 400\,000$

So the Sun is 400 000 times brighter than the Moon.

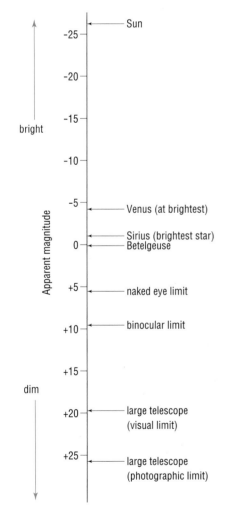

Fig 7.4   The apparent magnitudes of stars lie on a logarithmic scale.

7.3 For each of the following pairs, calculate how many times brighter the first object is than the second. (Apparent magnitudes *m* are given in brackets.)

(a) Venus (*m* = −4.4 at its brightest) and Jupiter (*m* = −2.7).

(b) Sirius (*m* = −1.46) and Betelgeuse (*m* = 0.50).

(c) Andromeda Galaxy (*m* = 4.8) and the Crab Nebula (*m* = 8.4).

Absolute magnitudes

In order to deduce how far away a star is, we want to compare its apparent brightness with its actual brightness. But what do we mean by 'actual brightness'? We define a quantity called the **absolute magnitude** of the star as follows:

We picture the star at a standard distance of 10 pc. Then we see how bright it appears on the apparent magnitude scale, and this is its absolute magnitude *M*.

In effect, this defines a fair test of the brightness of stars. We are comparing their brightnesses when they are all at a distance of 10 pc.

The absolute and apparent magnitudes of a star at a distance *d* are related by

$$m - M = 5 \log(d/10)$$

(In this equation, the 5 comes from 2 × 2.512; the 10 comes from 10 pc; logarithms are to base 10. A full derivation is given in Appendix B.2.)

Fig 7.5 shows what happens to the stars shown in Fig 7.4 when this equation is applied to their apparent magnitudes.

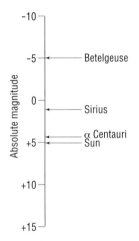

Fig 7.5 The brightest stars lie at the top of the scale of absolute magnitude.

Worked example

Alpha (α) Centauri has an apparent magnitude *m* of 0.1 and is at a distance of 1.32 pc. What is its absolute magnitude *M*?

Rearranging the equation relating *m* and *M* gives

$$
\begin{aligned}
M &= m - 5 \log(d/10) \\
&= 0.1 - 5 \log(0.132) \\
&= 0.1 - 5(-0.8790) \\
&= 0.1 + 4.397 \\
&= +4.497
\end{aligned}
$$

So the absolute magnitude of Alpha Centauri is 4.5. From Fig 7.5, you can see that this is very similar to the value for the Sun.

7.4 Use the data given in Table 7.2 to deduce which has the greater absolute magnitude, Sirius or Betelgeuse.

Table 7.2

Star	Apparent magnitude	Distance/pc
Sirius	−1.46	2.7
Betelgeuse	+0.50	94

Magnitude and distance

Now, how does our knowledge of the relationship between apparent and absolute magnitudes enable us to calculate the distance of stars? The principle is this:

From our discussion of the spectra of stars in Chapter 6, you will know that the spectrum of a star can give us an idea of its temperature and hence its luminosity. The relationship between spectra, temperature and brightness has been studied in great detail, and is discussed further in Chapter 8. The luminosity of a star is directly related to its absolute magnitude. So from its spectrum, we can get a good idea of a star's absolute magnitude. By comparing this with its apparent magnitude, we can deduce its distance.

We can rearrange the equation relating M and m to make the distance d its subject:

$$d = 10 \text{ pc} \times 10^{(m-M)/5}$$

This technique of spectroscopic parallax (or more accurately, comparing apparent and absolute magnitudes) is reasonably accurate to a distance of 10 Mpc (megaparsecs), enabling us to measure distances to nearby galaxies if individual stars can be picked out.

7.3 CEPHEID VARIABLE STARS

Beyond 10 megaparsecs

But what about distances beyond 10 Mpc? The use of spectroscopic parallax becomes less reliable. A more reliable technique makes use of variable stars.

For two centuries it has been known that some stars are variables; that is, their luminosity fluctuates regularly. The star Delta (δ) Cephei was discovered in 1784 by a young deaf mute amateur astronomer, John Goodricke. He recorded the apparent magnitude of the star, and noticed that the brightness varied between magnitudes 4.3 and 3.4 over a 5.4 day period as shown in Fig 7.6. For three-quarters of the cycle, the star's brightness is fading; then it rises to maximum brightness in 1.5 days.

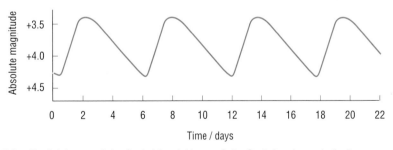

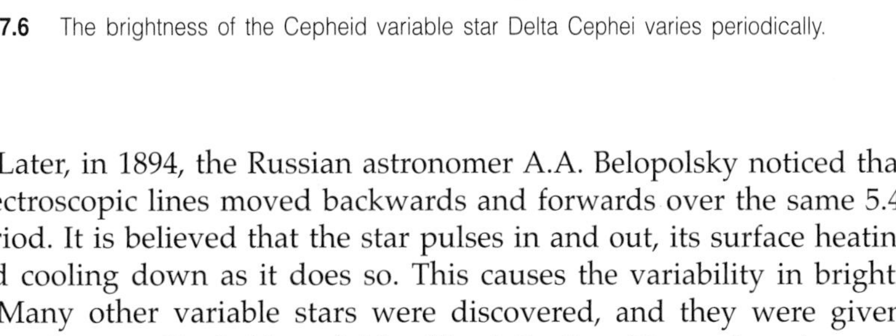

Fig 7.6   The brightness of the Cepheid variable star Delta Cephei varies periodically.

Later, in 1894, the Russian astronomer A.A. Belopolsky noticed that the spectroscopic lines moved backwards and forwards over the same 5.4 day period. It is believed that the star pulses in and out, its surface heating up and cooling down as it does so. This causes the variability in brightness.

Many other variable stars were discovered, and they were given the general name **Cepheid variable**. Henrietta Leavitt, an American astronomer (Fig 7.7), discovered an important point about these stars. She showed that there is a link between their absolute magnitude and their period. Once this was apparent, a calibration chart could be drawn up, as shown in Fig 7.8.

Fig 7.7   Henrietta Leavitt, the American astronomer who discovered the relationship between the period of a Cepheid variable and its absolute magnitude.

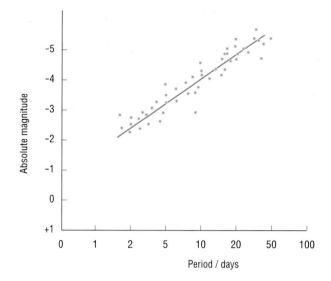

Fig 7.8 The longer the period of a Cepheid variable, the brighter it is.

It is relatively easy to measure the period of a variable star, and from this we can deduce its absolute magnitude. By comparing this with its apparent magnitude, we can calculate its distance. A dim Cepheid variable which pulses over a long period must be a bright star that is very distant rather than a dim star that is nearby.

The most luminous Cepheid variables have brightnesses that are equal to 100 000 Suns with periods of 100 days, whilst the dimmest are around 200 times brighter than our Sun with a period of around a day. The brightest variable stars can be detected in nearby galaxies. This gives astronomers a more accurate method than spectroscopic parallax in determining the distances to the galaxies. M31, the spiral galaxy in Andromeda, was originally thought to be 1500 000 ly away; however, Cepheid examination by Edwin Hubble in the 1920s suggested that it was considerably further away, at 2200 000 ly.

Cepheid variables are one type of 'standard candle'. Others include low-mass variable RR Lyrae stars, and certain types of supernovae (exploding stars) can also be used. The latter can be very useful as they can be used to estimate the distance to distant galaxies.

QUESTION

7.5 The graphs in Fig 7.9 show the variation of apparent magnitude of two Cepheid variable stars. Use the period–luminosity law to find the absolute magnitude of each star and then determine the distance to each of the stars.

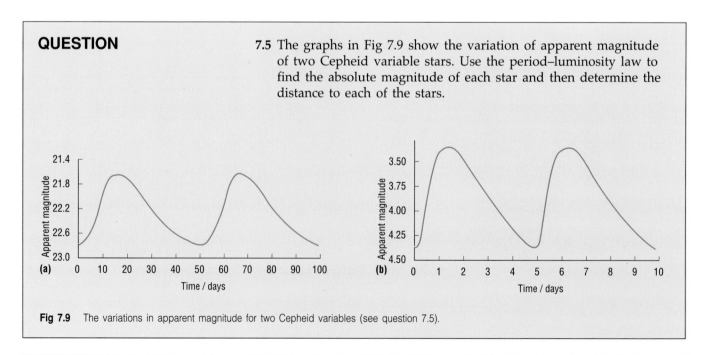

Fig 7.9 The variations in apparent magnitude for two Cepheid variables (see question 7.5).

7.4 RED-SHIFTS AND RECEIVING GALAXIES

Moving bodies

Yet another method for estimating astronomical distances is available for distant galaxies. This relies on observations of the absorption and emission lines in their spectra. It has been found, for many stars and galaxies, that these spectral lines do not occur at their 'correct' frequencies. The pattern of lines is correct, but they are displaced, usually towards the red (longer-wavelength) end of the spectrum. We say that the spectrum shows a **red-shift**. Fig 7.10 shows an example.

Fig 7.10 The line spectrum of a receding star shows a red-shift relative to that of a stationary star: **(a)** stationary star and **(b)** receding star.

The explanation for the red-shift lies in the motion of the star or galaxy. If it is moving away from the observer at a significant speed, then all its radiation will be red-shifted. Fig 7.11 shows why.

The picture shows two stars, each emitting a pulse of four waves. Star A is stationary, and its wave pulse occupies a length 4λ in space. Star B is moving away from the observer. Wave 1 is emitted while it is close to the observer; by the time it emits wave 4, it has moved some distance further away. So the four waves occupy a length greater than 4λ in space.

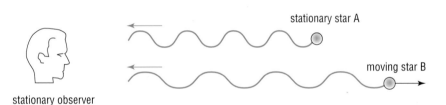

Fig 7.11 Waves from a receding source are 'stretched', causing the wavelength to be increased.

You can see from Fig 7.11 that the wavelength of the waves has increased by an amount $\Delta\lambda$. The greater the velocity v at which the star is receding, the greater will be the increase in wavelength. The change in wavelength is related to the velocity by the following equation:

$$\frac{\Delta\lambda}{\lambda} = \frac{v}{c}$$

where c is the speed of light. This relationship is derived in Appendix B.3. (Take care! $\Delta\lambda$ is a single quantity, the increase in wavelength; it does not mean $\Delta \times \lambda$.)

If the wavelength increases and the speed of light is constant, the frequency f must decrease (in the same proportion). The change in frequency Δf is given by:

$$\frac{\Delta f}{f} = -\frac{v}{c}$$

So the red-shift of spectral lines (the shift in their wavelength) can be used to determine the velocity of a moving star, galaxy or other astronomical object. A star whose spectral lines show a 10% increase in their wavelengths must be moving at 10% of the speed of light, away from the observer.

QUESTIONS

7.6 The light from a star that is moving towards the Earth will show a blue-shift. Draw a diagram (similar to Fig 7.11) to show why this is so.

7.7 The spectrum of a star is found to have a line in its hydrogen Balmer series at a wavelength of 686.8 nm. The same line, when measured on Earth, has a wavelength of 656.3 nm. At what speed is the star receding from the Earth?

[speed of light $c = 3 \times 10^8 \, \text{m s}^{-1}$]

Hubble's law

Red-shifts can help us to measure the speeds of stars and galaxies. But what has this to do with determining their distances?

The American astronomer Edwin Hubble (Fig 7.12), working in the 1920s, discovered a relationship between the velocity of recession of a galaxy and its distance from us. By plotting a graph of velocity of recession against distance, he was able to show a very dramatic relationship. The further away a galaxy is, the higher its velocity. A modern plot of this relationship is shown in Fig 7.13.

This was a truly extraordinary finding. It was known that stars and galaxies were moving around. However, Hubble showed that this motion is not random; in general, the galaxies are all moving apart. The graph of Fig 7.13 can be represented as an equation relating velocity v and distance d:

$$v = H_0 \times d$$

where H_0 is the Hubble constant. This equation is known as **Hubble's law**.

Now you should be able to see that, if we measure the red-shift of a galaxy, we can determine its velocity of recession, and from Hubble's law we can then determine its distance. This is most useful for distant galaxies.

Fig 7.12 Edwin Hubble, whose observations led astronomers to conclude that the Universe is expanding.

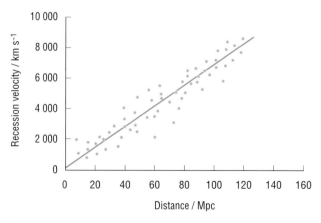

Fig 7.13 Hubble's law relates the velocity of recession of distant galaxies to their distance.

Compounding uncertainties

The Hubble constant tells us how the distance of a galaxy may be determined from its velocity of recession. Its value is rather uncertain, and is argued over hotly. It can be found from the gradient of the graph (Fig 7.13):

$$H_0 = (70 \pm 30) \text{ km s}^{-1} \text{ Mpc}^{-1}$$

Where does this large uncertainty come from? We have seen that there are several different techniques used for determining the distances of astronomical objects:

- Parallax, for nearby stars
- Spectroscopic parallax, for more distant stars
- Cepheid variables, for yet more distant stars and galaxies
- Red-shift analysis, for the most distant galaxies

Unfortunately, each of these techniques has its own uncertainties, and each depends for its calibration on the one before it. So, for example, if all our parallax measurements are wrong by 10%, then our spectroscopic parallax measurements will be wrong by as much, plus the uncertainty inherent in this technique. By the time we get to red-shift analysis and the Hubble constant, the uncertainties are large. Some astronomers believe that the Hubble constant's numerical value is about 50, others think it is closer to 100.

QUESTION

7.8 A distant galaxy is found to have a red-shift of 15%.
   (a) Calculate its velocity of recession.
   (b) Assuming a value for H_0 of 100 km s^{-1} Mpc^{-1}, deduce its distance.
   (c) If H_0 is taken to have a value of only 50 km s^{-1} Mpc^{-1}, deduce an alternative value for its distance.

Explaining Hubble's law

There are two reasons why the light from a star may show a red-shift:

- It may be moving away from us, through space. Many stars in our galaxy show such a red-shift. This is an example of the Doppler effect.
- Space itself may be expanding. If space expands, it carries the stars and galaxies with it, and they will all be seen to be receding from one another.

It is this second explanation which is thought to explain Hubble's law, and it has important consequences for our view of the Universe.

If we believe that space is expanding, it follows that, in the past, its volume was much smaller and everything was much closer together. In fact, it appears that, at some time in the past, everything in the Universe was compressed into a tiny space – perhaps even a point.

We will look at this further in Theme 3 of this book. However, for the present, we will look at what Hubble's law can tell us about the age of the Universe. If we consider one point on the graph, we can find how velocity and distance are related. For example, a galaxy at a distance of 100 Mpc is receding at about 7000 km s^{-1}. (This assumes a value for H_0

of 70 km s^{-1} Mpc^{-1}.) Given that 100 Mpc = 3.1×10^{21} km, how long will it have taken, at this speed, to travel this distance? We find

$$\text{time} = \frac{\text{distance}}{\text{speed}} = \frac{3.1 \times 10^{21} \text{ km}}{7000 \text{ km s}^{-1}} = 4.4 \times 10^{17} \text{ s}$$

This is approximately 14 000 million years, and this gives us an estimate of the age of the Universe.

Now you can see why the large uncertainty in the value of the Hubble constant H_0 is a problem. The uncertainty means that we cannot deduce distances accurately, and so we cannot deduce the age of the Universe to better than ±50%.

QUESTION

7.9 The Hubble constant is the gradient of the graph shown in Fig 7.13. The age of the Universe is equal to the reciprocal of this, i.e.

$$\text{age of Universe} = 1/H_0$$

Assuming values for H_0 of 50 and 100 km s^{-1} Mpc^{-1}, deduce two possible values for the age of the Universe.

7.5 MEASURING ROTATION

Using the Doppler effect

You will be familiar with the change in pitch of the siren of an emergency vehicle as it approaches and then passes you. The frequency is raised as it approaches, and then lowered as it recedes. You can observe the same effect with the engine noise of a passing motorcycle. These are examples of the **Doppler effect**, as is the red-shift of light from moving stars discussed above. The effect was first analysed by Christian Doppler in 1842.

In astronomy, the Doppler effect can be used in determining the following:

- Rotational period of the Sun and other stars
- Rotational period of a planet
- Orbital period of binary stars
- Recessional velocity of a distant star or galaxy

The rotation of the Sun

The Sun rotates; evidence for this comes from observations of sunspots, which move across its face as it spins. This means that, when we look at the Sun, one side (or limb) is moving towards us and the other side is moving away. We are observing light coming to us from a moving source, and the Doppler effect comes into play.

Fig 7.14 shows what happens. The right-hand side of the Sun's disc is moving away from us. If we focus a spectrometer on this point, the light we observe will be red-shifted. Lines in the Sun's spectrum will be shifted towards the red end of the spectrum. If we focus on the left-hand side, we are looking at a source of light that is moving towards us, and the light will be blue-shifted. If we look at the centre of the Sun's disc, the spectrum will be unaffected, as there is no motion towards or away from us.

Hence, by measuring the changes in frequency of the light coming from opposite sides of the Sun's disc, we can deduce how fast the Sun's surface is moving round.

MEASURING ASTRONOMICAL DISTANCES

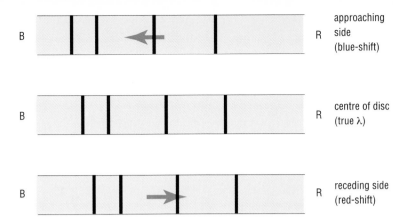

B | approaching side (blue-shift) R

B | centre of disc (true λ) R

B | receding side (red-shift) R

Fig 7.14 The Sun's rotation causes its spectrum to be shifted.

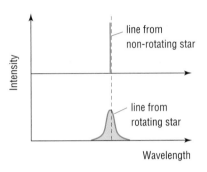

line from non-rotating star

line from rotating star

Fig 7.15 A spectral line from a distant star is broadened if the star is rotating.

As far as we know, all stars rotate. However, the Sun is the only star that appears to Earth-bound observers as a disc; all other stars appear as points of light. So we cannot focus our spectrometer on opposite sides of any other star. However, we can still see a consequence of the Doppler effect; if we concentrate on a single line in the star's spectrum, we find that it is spread out across a range of frequencies. The lowest frequency (longest wavelength) arises from light coming from the edge of the star that is receding from us. The highest frequency arises from light coming from the opposite, approaching edge. Fig 7.15 shows this **Doppler broadening** of a spectral line.

Thus we have a technique that allows us to determine the speed of rotation of stars and even of distant galaxies.

QUESTIONS

7.10 As described above, we can deduce the speed of rotation of the Sun by measuring the Doppler shift of lines in its spectrum. What else would we need to know to determine its *rate* of rotation, and hence its period of rotation?
[Hint: think about the circular motion equation $v = \omega r$.]

7.11 Fig 7.15 shows the effect of Doppler broadening on a spectral line for a rotating star. Copy the diagram and add to it:

(a) a similar line for a star that is rotating faster;

(b) the line for the same star, if it was moving rapidly away from the observer, as well as rotating.

Rotating planets

The planet Venus is blanketed by a thick, featureless atmosphere. Whilst it was comparatively easy to determine the length of its year, the length of a Venusian day remained unsolved until the middle of the 20th century. Indeed, for a long time it was thought that one side always faced the Sun, in the same way that one side of the Moon always faces the Earth.

In 1956, the American scientist Robert Richardson, using the telescope at Mount Wilson Observatory, measured the Doppler shift of spectral lines in sunlight reflected from the planet. He was able to show that Venus does indeed rotate, but only very slowly, so that its day length is 243 Earth days. Fig 7.16 shows the red-shift and blue-shift of sunlight reflected by the opposite edges of Venus.

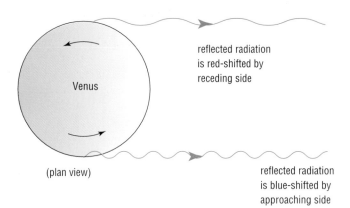

reflected radiation
is red-shifted by
receding side

Venus

(plan view)

reflected radiation
is blue-shifted by
approaching side

Fig 7.16 Light from Venus is Doppler shifted because of the planet's rotation.

Fig 7.17 A view of the surface of Venus, produced using radar techniques by the Magellan spacecraft.

Radar astronomy

It isn't always possible to observe the Doppler shift of light to determine the rotation of planets. Instead, radio waves may be used. Radio waves sent out from Earth are reflected back, in the same way that radar can be used on Earth to monitor the positions of aircraft, etc. This is radar astronomy. It can tell us two things:

- The distance to a planet can be found by measuring the time taken for a pulse of radio waves to travel out to the planet and back again.
- The speed of movement and rotation of a planet can be found by measuring the Doppler shift of the reflected waves.

Note that, when waves are reflected by a moving object, a double Doppler effect is observed. The shift in wavelength is twice as much as is observed for waves emitted by a moving source.

The Magellan spacecraft, launched in 1989, has carried out extensive radar surveys of the surface of Venus. (Radio waves can penetrate the planet's dense cloud cover.) The spacecraft transmits thousands of radio pulses each second down to the planet's surface and detects the reflected waves. These data are analysed by computers on Earth, which have been able to build up a detailed picture of the planet, with a resolution of 250 m. Fig 7.17 shows one such computer-generated image.

QUESTIONS

7.12 Venus has a diameter of 12 100 km and a rotational period of 243 days.

  (a) Calculate its angular velocity ω, and hence its speed of rotation v.

  (b) Radio waves of wavelength 1.0 m are used to determine its speed of rotation. Calculate the expected shift in wavelength $\Delta\lambda$ for waves reflected at opposite edges of Venus's disc.

$$[c = 3 \times 10^8 \text{ m s}^{-1}]$$

7.13 Pluto, the furthest planet in the Solar System, is too distant for astronomers to be able to direct radio waves onto opposite sides of its disc. Suggest how radar astronomy could still be used to determine its period of rotation.

[Hint: think about spectral broadening.]

Binary stars

Our Sun is a relatively unusual star. Only about 40% of stars are single stars like the Sun. Most stars are actually pairs called **binary stars**, and some are groups of three or more stars.

In a binary pair, the stars are attracted by each other's gravity. They orbit around a common centre of mass. Fig 7.18 shows how they move. If the two stars have the same mass, they travel round a common orbit. If, as is more usual, their masses are different, they travel around different orbits centred on the centre of mass of the pair.

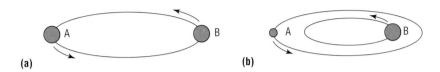

Fig 7.18   Binary stars orbit about their common centre of mass: **(a)** two stars of equal mass; **(b)** two stars of different masses.

The closest binary stars can be observed with powerful telescopes. A good example is Alpha Centauri, which has components of magnitudes 0.0 and 1.7 that take 80 years to orbit, making it an easy binary to distinguish. Obviously visual separation becomes more difficult if the stars are more distant or closer together. In such cases their spectra can be used to deduce the presence of two stars. These are called **spectroscopic binary stars**.

As the stars move around their centre of mass, one star will be approaching as the other is receding – see Fig 7.19. As star A approaches, its spectral lines will be blue-shifted. Light from star B is red-shifted. Their spectral lines will coincide as they pass across our line of view; then the shifts reverse.

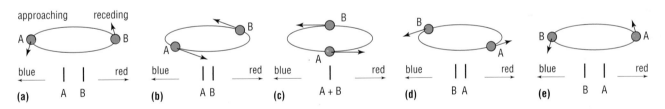

Fig 7.19   Doppler shifting of a spectral line for a binary pair of stars that share a single orbit, because their masses are equal.

From these observations the period T and velocities of the stars can be determined. If we know T and the separation r of the two stars, we can deduce their combined mass M:

$$M = \frac{4\pi^2 r^3}{GT^2}$$

Here, G is the universal gravitational constant (Chapter 2). You should recognise this relationship; it is the equation for Kepler's third law of planetary motion, derived in section 2.3.

For **optical binary stars**, we can measure the radii of the orbits of the individual stars. We know that the more massive star of a pair has a smaller radius of orbit; in fact, the radius is in inverse proportion to the star's mass. Hence knowing the combined masses of the two stars and the ratio of their orbital radii, we can work out their individual masses.

7.14 Fig 7.18(b) shows two stars of different masses that form a binary pair.
 (a) Which star travels fastest around its orbit?
 (b) Fig 7.20 shows how the red-shift of a particular spectral line varies as the stars orbit one another. (The curves are sine curves.) Which of the two curves is for the smaller star? Give a reason for your answer.

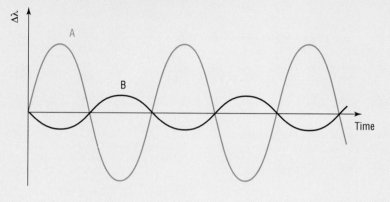

Fig 7.20 Variation in the Doppler shift of a spectral line for a binary pair of different masses (see question 7.14).

SUMMARY

Stellar distances can be deduced from measurements of parallax, spectroscopic parallax, the periods of Cepheid variable stars and the red-shifting of their light.

Each technique relies on the previous ones for calibration; this makes for large uncertainties in the largest distances.

The magnitude scale is used to classify the brightness of stars. Apparent magnitude m is a measure of the visual brightness of a star. Absolute magnitude M is the brightness of a star if it were to be placed at 10 pc from our Solar System.

Cepheid variables are stars whose luminosity is linked to their period of light variation. As their intrinsic brightness is known, their distance can be calculated. Cepheid stars can be seen in other galaxies.

The Doppler effect causes an increase in the wavelength of radiation if the source is moving away. This is known as a red-shift. The Doppler effect can be used in determining the rotational period of the planets and stars, including binary stars.

From measurements of the red-shifts of distant galaxies, Hubble deduced his law:

recessional velocity = Hubble constant (H_0) × distance

The reciprocal of the Hubble constant gives an estimate for the age of the Universe.

T2.1

(a) An astronomical telescope, consisting of a thin converging objective lens of focal length f_o and a thin converging eyepiece lens of focal length f_e, is set up in normal adjustment by an observer to view a distant object.

    (i) Show, by means of a labelled ray diagram, how a magnified image is formed by the telescope. The diagram should show the paths through the telescope of at least **two** rays from a non-axial point on the object.

    (ii) Defining the *angular magnification M* as

$$M = \frac{\text{angle subtended at the unaided eye by the object}}{\text{angle subtended at the eye by the final image}}$$

    show that

$$M = \frac{f_o}{f_e}$$

    (iii) If the separation of the lenses in the above telescope is 26 cm and $M = 12$, calculate the values of f_o and f_e.

(b) **(i)** State, without the aid of a ray diagram, how the eye-ring in an astronomical telescope is formed. Calculate its position for the telescope described in (a) (iii).

    (ii) Show that f_o and f_e are related to d_1 and d_2, the respective diameters of the objective lens and eye-ring, by the expression

$$\frac{f_o}{f_e} = \frac{d_1}{d_2}$$

    (iii) Assuming the observer's eye is placed at the eye-ring, estimate the minimum diameter of the objective lens of the telescope necessary for maximum light to enter the eye.

(c) Give **two** similarities between a dish radio telescope and an optical reflecting telescope.

(NEAB 1995)

T2.2

(a) Describe, with the aid of a diagram, a Newtonian reflecting telescope. The diagram should show the paths of **two** parallel rays from a point on a distant object to the eyepiece lens.

(b) Giving reasons for your answer, state **two** optical advantages, other than those involving aberrations, which a large reflecting telescope has over a large refracting telescope.

(NEAB 1990)

T2.3

(a) (i) Discuss the differences between radio telescopes and optical telescopes which arise from the different wavelengths of electromagnetic radiation detected.

(ii) State what factors determine the largest and smallest wavelengths at which a ground-based telescope can be used.

(b) Describe the mode of operation of a charge coupled device (CCD) used as a detector in a telescope. Give **two** advantages of using a CCD rather than a photographic plate as a detector.

(c) A CCD is placed at the focal point of a reflecting dish of a telescope. If the dish has a diameter of 2 m and is used to detect radiation of 400 nm wavelength, calculate the smallest angle the dish can resolve. Hence deduce the spacing of the detectors in the CCD if the focal length of the dish is 4 m.

(NEAB 1990)

T2.4

The electromagnetic spectrum encompasses various types of radiation. These have been used to carry out scientific studies on the Universe. With reference to the regions listed, describe how they are used and what information can be deduced:

(a) visible light from the Sun,
(b) radio waves,
(c) X-rays.

(UCLES December 1993)

T2.5

(a) The mean distance of the Earth from the Sun is 1.496×10^{11} m. The distance is called the astronomical unit. Explain briefly the particular significance of this distance for astronomers.

The star Sirius A has a parallax of 0.377 seconds of arc. Explain, with the aid of a labelled diagram, the meaning of the term *parallax*.

Calculate the distance of Sirius A from the Earth.

Explain how the velocity of Sirius A towards or away from the Earth can be found.

(b) Sirius A, a massive main sequence white star, is the brightest star in the sky. Sirius A has a faint companion, Sirius B, which is a white dwarf.

Explain the term *white dwarf*.

How would you account for the differences between Sirius A and Sirius B assuming that the two stars are roughly the same age?

(ULEAC January 1996 Specimen Paper)

T2.6

(a) Explain what is meant by

(i) *apparent magnitude* of a star,

(ii) *absolute magnitude* of a star.

State how they are related.

The table shows the absolute magnitude and apparent magnitude of the stars Rigel and Procyon.

Star	Absolute magnitude	Apparent magnitude
Rigel	−7.0	+0.1
Procyon	+2.7	+0.4

By considering the data for each star individually, deduce, without numerical calculation but giving your reasoning, which star is the furthest from Earth.

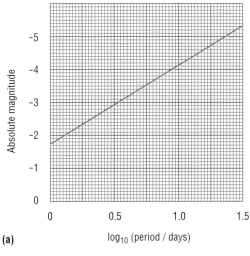

(a) $\log_{10}$ (period / days)

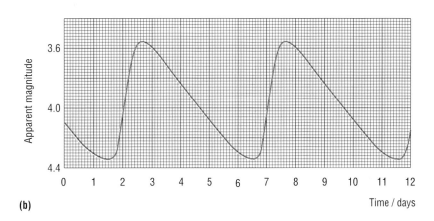

(b) Time / days

Fig T2.6 Diagrams for question T2.6.

(b) Fig T2.6(a) shows the correlation between the absolute magnitude and the period of pulsation for Cepheid variables. Fig T2.6(b) shows the variation in the apparent magnitude of Delta Cephei.

From the information in the figures, and using the mean value of the apparent magnitude, estimate the distance of Delta Cephei from Earth.

State why a parallax method cannot be used to measure the distance of Delta Cephei from Earth.

(NEAB 1987)

T2.7

(a) Explain how observation of reflected radar pulses from the surface of Venus can be used to measure

   (i) the distance of Venus from the Earth,

   (ii) the velocity of a point on the surface of Venus at its equator.

(b) Explain why the surface features of Venus cannot be mapped using an optical telescope but can be mapped using a radar method.

(c) A radio telescope with a dish aerial is modified to transmit and receive radar pulses of short duration.

When the aerial is pointed directly at Venus, the time elapsing between the transmission of a radar pulse and the reception of the reflected pulse from Venus has a minimum value of 280 seconds. If the experiment is repeated later, the time interval between transmission of a pulse and reception of the reflected pulse reaches a maximum value of 1720 seconds. After a further period the time interval is again found to be at its minimum value.

Give expressions for the minimum and maximum distances between the Earth and Venus in terms of their orbital radii, and hence determine the radius of the orbits of Venus and the Earth, assuming that both orbits are in the same plane, concentric and circular.

[The speed of electromagnetic waves *in vacuo* = 3.00×10^8 m s^{-1}]

(NEAB 1983)

Theme 3

STARS, GALAXIES AND THE BIG BANG

In the previous theme, we explored how astronomers observe the Universe, and how they use the information gained from their observations. In this final theme, astrophysics comes into its own.

What is the energy source of the stars? What are black holes, and will our Sun ever become one? How certain can we be that the Universe began with a Big Bang? This theme aims to apply the laws of physics to the Universe and all that is in it, to provide answers to these questions.

Gravity is the force that acts to hold galaxies together in large clusters. It is also the force that allows us to predict the existence of black holes. This picture from the Hubble Space Telescope shows stars forming in the Eagle Nebula as gravity pulls dust clouds (the gaseous 'pillars') together.

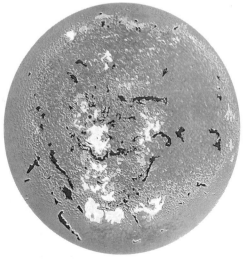

Nuclear forces are at work in the Sun, and cause sunspots and active regions. Physicists' knowledge of the processes at work on the microscopic scale of the atomic nucleus have allowed us to explain the life-cycle of stars, as well as what happened in the early stages of the evolution of the Universe.

Chapter 8

HOW STARS FORM

A star can have a lifetime of billions of years. For most of this time it changes very slowly. When we look out at the stars, we see stars at different stages of their lives, but we cannot see these very slow changes occurring. This chapter looks at what we know about how stars evolve during the course of their lives, and how we know it.

LEARNING OBJECTIVES

After studying this chapter you should be able to:

1. use the Hertzsprung–Russell diagram to discuss the different groups of stars;

2. describe the formation and development of a star;

3. describe how the fusion of hydrogen produces energy in a main-sequence star;

4. calculate the energy released in a fusion process;

5. understand the conditions necessary for fusion to take place;

6. estimate the temperatures required for the fusion of different nuclei;

7. understand the relationship between luminosity, mass and lifetime for a main-sequence star.

8.1 THE HERTZSPRUNG–RUSSELL DIAGRAM

Classifying stars

In Chapter 6, we saw how stars can be classified according to their temperature, colour and luminosity. In this chapter, we will see how this can help us to classify stars so that we can find out something about how they evolve. The current theory of how stars evolve is a theory based on observations; the difficulty we have in developing this theory is that our observations extend over a few centuries of modern astronomy, whereas the evolution of stars takes place over billions of years. We can observe stars at various stages of evolution, but what order do they come in? The problem is analogous to looking at a group of people of all ages and trying to place them in age order.

Perhaps the first scientist to recognise that certain patterns occur was the Danish astronomer Ejnar Hertzsprung, in the first decade of the 20th century. A decade later the American astronomer Henry Norris Russell carried out similar work, independently coming up with similar ideas. The result of the work of both men is the diagram that bears the men's names, the **Hertzsprung–Russell diagram**. This plots the luminosity (or absolute magnitude) against spectral type (or temperature). One version is shown in Fig 8.1.

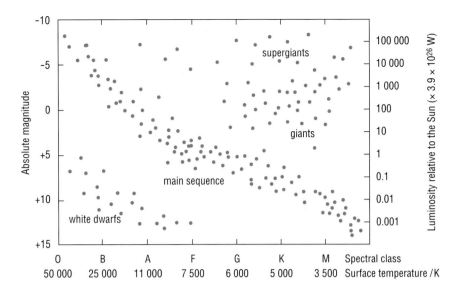

Fig 8.1 The Hertzsprung–Russell diagram is a way of representing the different populations of stars observed in the night sky.

To produce a modern version of this diagram, many stars are classified according to their luminosity and temperature. Then each star is plotted as a point on the diagram.

Notice the scales that are used. The *x* axis has a non-uniform temperature scale, increasing to the left. The *y* axis has a logarithmic scale of luminosity. (This is the same as absolute magnitude decreasing upwards.) Once we have examined the patterns within the Hertzsprung–Russell diagram, the scales will make more sense.

Most stars lie along a curve through the centre of the diagram, referred to as the **main sequence**. Since most stars belong to the main sequence, it would seem logical to deduce that stars spend most of their lifetime in this region. It is worth noting that the main sequence extends from very luminous blue stars (top left) to very dim red stars (bottom right), two very different types of star, as we shall see later.

Away from the main sequence, to the upper right of the diagram, lie two distinct groups of stars. Both groups of stars are quite cool, so we can deduce that they must emit a relatively small amount of light per unit surface area. However, to be as bright as they are, they must have a very large surface area. Hence they are referred to as **red giants** and **red supergiants**. Their surface temperatures are of the order of 3000–4000 K. Red giants are quite numerous in comparison to the significantly larger red supergiants. A red giant such as Betelgeuse, if it were placed in our Solar System, would encompass all the planets as far as the orbit of Jupiter.

Lastly there is a third distinct group of stars, which lie in the lower left corner of the Hertzsprung–Russell diagram. These are hot stars that appear dim. We know they are hot as the spectrum reveals strong Balmer lines; therefore their lack of luminosity suggests a very small diameter. These stars are known as **white dwarfs**. Such stars contain a mass roughly equal to that of the Sun within a volume similar to that of the Earth. Previously, white dwarfs were thought to be relatively rare. Now it is known that they are quite common, but difficult to observe.

QUESTIONS

8.1 Explain how we can deduce from the Hertzsprung–Russell diagram that stars which appear at the bottom left of the diagram must be hot and small.

8.2 Table 8.1 lists several stars, together with their absolute magnitudes and surface temperatures. Make a rough copy of the Hertzsprung–Russell diagram in Fig 8.1, and mark on it the position of each star. Use this to decide which group each star belongs to: main sequence, red giants, red supergiants or white dwarfs.

Table 8.1 Magnitudes and temperatures of some stars

Star	Luminosity (relative to Sun = 1)	Surface temperature/K
Sun	1.0	5 800
Betelgeuse	20 000	3 000
Aldebaran	200	4 700
Regulus	200	14 000
Rigel	20 000	13 000
Sirius B	0.002	20 000

8.2 STAR BIRTH

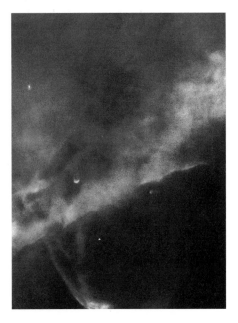

Fig 8.2 A gas cloud in the Orion nebula, thought to be the birth-place of new stars.

Gravitational collapse

If you look at the night sky with a telescope, you will see stars and planets. A close look will also reveal **gas clouds** as shown in Fig 8.2.

These gas clouds are thought to be the birth-place of stars. Interstellar space is not a perfect vacuum, as you might expect. Rather, it is a low-density mixture of atoms, molecules and microscopic specks of dust. In places these form greater concentrations, which appear as large dust clouds. The most common elements present are hydrogen and helium.

The density of these clouds is typically of the order of 1–10 atoms per cubic centimetre (the air in the room you are in having $\sim 10^{19}$ atoms in the same volume!). Ironically most of this interstellar gas comes from the death throes of earlier stars, which have blown themselves apart in supernovae, so enriching the interstellar medium. (Supernovae are discussed in section 9.3.)

Despite the extreme tenuousness of these clouds, gravitation is the predominant force that acts on the particles. This pulls the particles together, and they accelerate inwards. They collide increasingly frequently, sharing their energy. The temperature of the gas rises. Thus gravitational energy is converted to thermal energy.

A cloud of only a few solar masses is very unlikely to be cold and dense enough to collapse into a star. Star formation generally takes place in large clouds that are relatively dense and have regions of non-uniform density. As they collapse, they fragment to form **clusters**. This idea is supported by the fact that it is unusual to find young stars that are not in clusters. Dense clouds have masses typically hundreds or thousands of times that of the Sun.

QUESTION

8.3 Describe the energy changes that occur when a cloud of cold gaseous material collapses under gravity to become a denser, hotter cloud. In your answer, refer to gravitational potential energy, kinetic energy and thermal energy.

Protostars

When the gas cloud collapses sufficiently, it will be hot enough to emit significant amounts of infrared radiation. It is now described as a **protostar**, although its temperature is still too low for nuclear fusion to take place. Some radiation escapes to the surrounding space, but not enough to prevent the centre of the cloud from heating up further. Collisions between particles become increasingly energetic, so that first molecules and then atoms are disrupted, producing a plasma (a state of matter where, owing to the high temperature, atomic nuclei are stripped of some or all of their electrons, leaving a mixture of positive and negative ions).

Eventually an **ignition temperature** is reached, which initiates nuclear fusion, the process in which light atoms join together. This process is the source of energy for all true stars. The ignition temperature is of the order of a few million kelvins. The onset of fusion slows the contraction and the newly born star begins its time on the main sequence.

Very-low-mass protostars are unlikely to generate sufficient temperatures to trigger nuclear fusion. Nevertheless, they will still generate heat, and eventually become **brown dwarfs**. These are in a sense 'stars that didn't quite make it'.

Life before the main sequence

A star such as our Sun would have taken around 1000 years to have coalesced from a cloud to a protostar of around 20 solar diameters, by which time its luminosity would have been around 100 times that at the present. For more massive stars, the pre-main-sequence period is shorter, because greater gravitational forces lead to swifter star formation.

Fig 8.3 shows how stars of different masses evolve before they reach

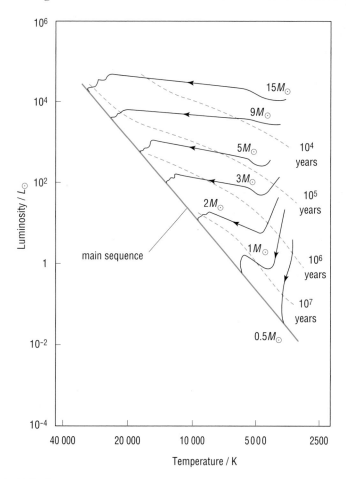

Fig 8.3 The early evolution of a star depends on its mass. The black lines show how the temperature and luminosity change for young stars of different masses.

the main sequence. This diagram focuses on the main-sequence region of the Hertzsprung–Russell diagram. The black lines show the evolutionary paths of protostars of different masses, whilst the dotted lines show the length of time spent in the pre-main-sequence period. Notice that heavy stars evolve much faster. A star whose mass is 15 solar masses ($15M_\odot$) takes only 100 000 years to reach the main sequence, whilst a $0.5M_\odot$ star takes more than 10 000 000 years.

QUESTION

8.4 Use the diagram (Fig 8.3) to describe the evolution of a star of mass equal to that of the Sun, during its life before it reaches the main sequence. Describe how its temperature and luminosity change during this time.

8.3 FUSION IN A MAIN-SEQUENCE STAR

Fusion in the Sun

Our Sun is a fairly typical main-sequence star, which lies much closer to us than any other star. We will look at its energy production processes. Later, we will consider how other stars may differ if they are of a different spectral class, mass or age.

In the Sun, hydrogen nuclei are converted into helium nuclei by the process of **nuclear fusion**. (This is the mechanism involved in the explosive energy production in a hydrogen bomb.)

The Sun consists largely of hydrogen nuclei (protons), since, at the high temperatures which prevail, the electrons have been stripped from the hydrogen atoms. These hydrogen nuclei repel one another because of the electrostatic force between their positive charges. However, if they are moving fast enough, this repulsive force can be overcome by the strong **nuclear force** that holds nuclei together. If this occurs, the hydrogen nuclei can bind together. This is a more stable configuration, and energy is released in the process.

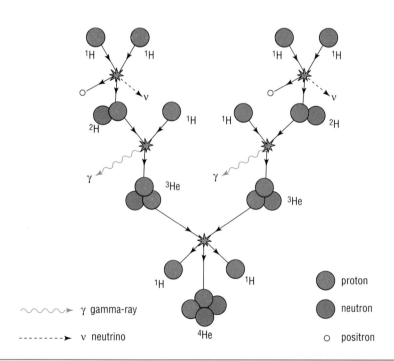

Fig 8.4 The proton–proton chain, the mechanism whereby hydrogen nuclei fuse to form helium.

$\sim\!\!\sim\!\!\sim\!\!\rightarrow$ γ gamma-ray

$\text{-----}\!\rightarrow$ ν neutrino

proton

neutron

○ positron

Fig 8.4 shows the stages in the proton–proton chain that lead to the formation of a helium nucleus and the release of energy. The overall reaction involves four protons fusing together to form a single helium nucleus; two positrons and two neutrinos are released, along with some energy. (Positrons e^+ are positively charged electrons; neutrinos v are tiny, uncharged particles of negligible mass.) The energy released is in two forms: kinetic energy of the particles, and gamma photons. We can represent the reaction with a single equation:

$$4{}^1\text{H} \rightarrow {}^4\text{He} + 2e^+ + 2v + \text{energy}$$

In section 3.6, we saw that, when a stable nucleus is formed from its constituent nucleons, the mass of the system decreases by an amount Δm, and a corresponding amount of energy E is released. These are related by Einstein's famous equation

$$E = \Delta m \times c^2$$

where c is the speed of light, $3 \times 10^8 \text{ m s}^{-1}$.

So we can find how much energy is released by calculating how much mass disappears in the reaction. Relevant masses are shown in Table 8.2.

The decrease in mass is given by

$$\Delta m = 4 \times 1.673 \times 10^{-27} - (6.6465 \times 10^{-27} + 2 \times 9.11 \times 10^{-31})$$
$$= 4.37 \times 10^{-29} \text{ kg}$$

and the energy released is therefore

$$E = 4.37 \times 10^{-29} \times (3 \times 10^8)^2$$
$$= 3.93 \times 10^{-12} \text{ J}$$

This may appear to be a very small amount of energy. However, a large number of nuclei are going through this reaction every second, so the amount of energy becomes significant. The power output of the Sun is 3.83×10^{26} W, and from this we can calculate the number of reactions that occur and the mass converted every second:

$$\text{number of reactions per second} = \frac{\text{power of Sun}}{\text{energy released per reaction}}$$

$$= \frac{3.83 \times 10^{26} \text{ W}}{3.93 \times 10^{-12} \text{ J}}$$

$$= 9.75 \times 10^{37} \text{ reactions per second}$$

and (remembering that $1 \text{ W} = 1 \text{ J s}^{-1}$)

$$\text{mass converted per second} = \frac{3.83 \times 10^{26} \text{ J}}{(3 \times 10^8 \text{ m s}^{-1})^2}$$

$$= 4.3 \times 10^9 \text{ kg s}^{-1}$$

$$= 4.3 \text{ million tonnes per second}$$

Table 8.2 Particles and masses

Particle	Mass/kg
proton ^{1}H	1.673×10^{-27}
helium nucleus ^{4}He	6.6465×10^{-27}
positron e^+	9.11×10^{-31}
neutrino v	negligible

QUESTION

8.5 From the data given above, make an estimate of the lifetime of the Sun. You should assume the following:

- The fusion of hydrogen to form helium is the only reaction that occurs (it isn't).
- The Sun was initially 75% hydrogen by mass (as was probably the case).
- It will continue to shine until 10% of the hydrogen has been fused.

So the Sun is losing mass at a rate of more than four million tonnes a second! This sounds quite frightening. However, the Sun has a mass of 2×10^{30} kg, and it will last for many years to come.

High-temperature fusion

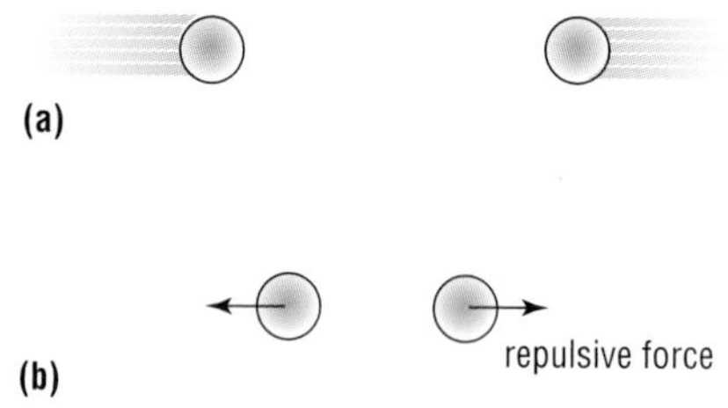

Nuclear fusion requires very high temperatures – millions of degrees – if it is to occur. We can estimate the necessary temperature by thinking about what happens when two nuclei fuse.

Two hydrogen nuclei (protons) repel one another, because each has a positive charge. To overcome this, they must be moving very fast, so that they can approach sufficiently closely for the strong nuclear force to hold them together – see Fig 8.5.

We can estimate the necessary temperature by thinking about the energy changes involved. When the particles are a long way apart, they have kinetic energy E_k. As they approach, they slow down. Kinetic energy is being changed to electrostatic potential energy E_p. Fusion will occur if the two protons approach within about 10^{-14} m of one another.

We will calculate the electrostatic potential energy of a proton at this distance from a second proton. Then we will calculate the temperature needed to give it this energy.

The electrostatic potential energy of a charge Q_1 at a distance r from a second charge Q_2 is given by

$$E_p = \frac{1}{4\pi\varepsilon_0} \frac{Q_1 Q_2}{r}$$

where $\varepsilon_0 = 8.85 \times 10^{-12}$ F m^{-1} is the permittivity of free space. In this case, the two charges are the same:

$$Q_1 = Q_2 = +1.6 \times 10^{-19} \text{ C}$$

For fusion just to occur, the proton's kinetic energy must be equal to E_p. Now, the kinetic energy of a particle is related to its absolute temperature T by the following relationship:

$$E_k = \frac{3}{2} kT$$

where $k = 1.38 \times 10^{-23}$ J K^{-1} is the Boltzmann constant. (You will be familiar with this relationship if you have studied the kinetic theory of gases.)

Now we equate the proton's kinetic energy (when it is moving freely about) with its potential energy (when it is about to fuse with a second proton):

$$E_k = E_p$$

So

$$\frac{3}{2} kT = \frac{1}{4\pi\varepsilon_0} \frac{Q_1 Q_2}{r}$$

Rearranging to find T gives

$$T = \frac{2Q_1 Q_2}{12k\pi\varepsilon_0 r}$$

and substituting in numerical values gives

$$T = \frac{(1.6 \times 10^{-19})^2}{6 \times 1.38 \times 10^{-23} \times \pi \times 8.85 \times 10^{-12} \times 10^{-14}} = 1.11 \times 10^9 \text{ K}$$

Fig 8.5 **(a)** Two fast-moving protons have kinetic energy. **(b)** As they approach one another, they slow down; their energy changes to electrostatic potential energy.

(a)

(b)

repulsive force

So our rough estimate is that fusion cannot occur until the temperature reaches about 10^9 K. In fact, fusion can take place at somewhat greater separations than that suggested above, owing to quantum-mechanical effects, so fusion usually starts when a star heats up to temperatures in the range of 10^7 to 10^8 K. These conditions only occur at the centre of stars.

QUESTION

8.6 Stars fuse elements other than hydrogen. For example, they can fuse two helium nuclei:

$$^4He + {}^4He \rightarrow {}^8Be + \gamma$$

Here, γ is a gamma photon. Will this reaction require a higher or lower temperature if it is to occur? Give a reason to support your answer.

8.4 THE LIFE OF A MAIN-SEQUENCE STAR

Convection and radiation

The energy from nuclear fusion is generated at the core of a star. However, the light we receive on the Earth emanates from the Sun's surface. So how does the energy travel to the surface (a distance of 600 000 km in the case of the Sun)?

There are three methods of thermal energy (heat) transfer: conduction, convection and radiation. As most stars are gaseous, conduction is not very significant. In practice, the other two mechanisms are both involved, as shown in Fig 8.6.

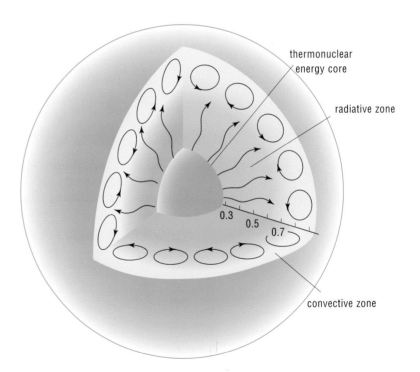

Fig 8.6 Energy radiates outwards from the core of the Sun; near the surface, convection currents carry energy outwards.

Nuclear fusion mainly occurs in the core of a star. For the Sun, this is the central region, with a radius of about one-quarter of the star's radius. Here, high-energy **photons** (packets of light energy) are produced, and they radiate outwards. Because of the high density of the gases in the innermost parts of stars, these photons are absorbed and re-emitted as

Fig 8.7 A close look at the surface of the Sun shows granular structures. This Doppler image reveals the presence of convection currents welling up towards the surface.

lower-energy photons on the route outwards. One high-energy photon at the core may result in 1600 photons of visible light at the surface. Because some of these photons are radiated back towards the centre, the whole process can take about one million years!

The gas in outer parts of a star is cooler, and this increases the opacity (the resistance to radiation). Consequently, beyond about 0.8 of the Sun's radius, convection takes over. Rising currents of hot gas give rise to the granular appearance of the Sun's surface, as shown in Fig 8.7. The effect is rather analogous to the convection cells seen when a substance such as jam or tomato soup is boiling.

Mass, luminosity and lifetime

As long as a protostar has a mass between 0.08 and 60–100 solar masses, fusion will start up and a star will become a main-sequence star. The star will spend most of its life in this region of the Hertzsprung–Russell diagram.

The lifetime of a star in the main sequence is linked to its luminosity and mass because:

- The greater its mass, the longer it will last before its supply of hydrogen is used up.

- The greater its luminosity, the sooner it will use up its supply of hydrogen.

When stars form from clouds of gas in space, their composition is initially 73% hydrogen, 25% helium and 2% other elements (by mass). During their main-sequence lifetime, energy is generated by the proton–proton chain until the hydrogen reserves run low. Our Sun is already around five billion (5×10^9) years old. It has more helium than hydrogen at its core; never-

ASSIGNMENT

Table 8.3 shows the relationship between mass, temperature, luminosity and lifetime for main-sequence stars. Plot suitable graphs of these data, and try to determine any mathematical relationships between these quantities. [You may find that logarithmic graphs are most appropriate.]

Use your graphs to help you answer the following question:

8.7 Sirius A, one of our nearest-neighbour stars, has a mass of 2.46 solar masses and is 23.4 times more luminous than the Sun. Estimate its lifetime on the main sequence, and show that Sirius A must be quite a new star in cosmic terms.

Table 8.3 Lifetimes of main-sequence stars[a]

Mass/$M_\odot$	Surface temperature/K	Luminosity/$L_\odot$	Lifetime on main sequence/10^6 years
25	35 000	80 000	3
15	30 000	10 000	15
3	11 000	60	500
1.5	7000	5	3 000
1.0	6000	1	10 000
0.75	5000	0.5	15 000
0.50	4000	0.03	200 000

[a]Note: masses are given in units of solar masses, $M_\odot$; luminosities in solar luminosities, $L_\odot$.

HOW STARS FORM

theless, it still has enough hydrogen to maintain its present level of energy production for another five billion years. After this, the structure of the Sun will change substantially, as will the fusion reactions.

So the Sun's lifetime is likely to be about 10^{10} years. (You should have come to a similar conclusion in your answer to question 8.5 above.) The age of the Sun is comparable with the best estimate of the age of the Earth, 4.6 billion years, from studies of the radioactivity of the oldest rocks. It is also somewhat shorter than the age of the Universe, as estimated from the Hubble constant (section 7.4).

SUMMARY

The Hertzsprung–Russell diagram is used to show the different populations of stars that are observed.

Gravity causes gas clouds to contract until they heat up sufficiently for fusion to start.

Fusion requires very high temperatures and pressures to overcome the electrostatic repulsion between hydrogen nuclei.

Main-sequence stars fuse hydrogen to form helium, releasing energy in the process.

The lifetime of a star depends on its mass and luminosity.

Chapter 9

HOW STARS DIE

The previous chapter took us through stellar evolution from star birth to the star's life in the main sequence. This chapter examines the changes that occur in a star's old age.

LEARNING OBJECTIVES

After studying this chapter you should be able to:

1. explain how mass affects the development of stars after the main sequence;

2. understand the mechanisms involved in the formation of a red giant star;

3. explain how white dwarf stars, neutron stars and black holes are formed;

4. outline the evidence for the existence of black holes;

5. apply some of the results of general relativity to black holes.

9.1 THE FORMATION OF A RED GIANT STAR

After the main sequence

You will recall from the Hertzsprung–Russell diagram that, in the top right-hand corner, there are two populations of cool, bright stars, the red giants and red supergiants. These are stars which have completed their lives in the main sequence; in fact, almost all stars become red giants after their main-sequence lives. Only the very-low-mass **red dwarf stars** escape this fate. The most massive stars become supergiants. So what causes the transformation?

A main-sequence star is rather like a bonfire. Hydrogen fuses to leave helium embers at the centre. These helium embers are not hot enough to fuse to other elements, whilst outside the core there is a shell of 'unburnt' hydrogen, since the pressures and temperatures are insufficient for fusion of hydrogen. Since convection is not present in the central regions of a star, there is no circulation of gases. (Of course, to talk of 'burning' in a star is simply a figure of speech. Burning is a chemical process involving oxidation; fusion is a nuclear process.)

As the fusion of hydrogen in the core dies down, the outward expansive pressure decreases. The gravitational forces start to dominate, and this results in the contraction of the core. Now the pressure in the core increases, and its temperature rises to a point where the fusion of helium is initiated.

Shell burning, the fusion of hydrogen surrounding the core, occurs because of the increased temperature and density due to gravitational contraction. Consequently, there is more helium available and the size of the core increases. Over a few million years, a short period in stellar terms, the star reaches a situation where it is unstable, with the outer regions swelling outwards and the core contracting. The star has become a **red giant**.

The star's position on the Hertzsprung–Russell diagram has dramatically changed. Its surface area has increased and its temperature has decreased. Typically, a red giant may have a diameter 25 times that of the Sun, over 30 million kilometres, whilst the surface temperature may be only 3000–4000°C. So how does its luminosity change?

Recall Stefan's law, discussed in Chapter 6. This states that the luminosity L is given by the expression

$$L = \sigma A T^4$$

The star's temperature has fallen by perhaps 30%; however, its surface area has increased by perhaps 500 times. The overall effect is to increase the star's luminosity by a factor of at least 100.

Recall also Wien's law:

$$\lambda_{max} T = 0.002\,89\ \text{m K}$$

The reduction of the star's temperature will increase the dominant wavelength of the light it emits, moving it to the red end of the spectrum. The star will move to the top right-hand corner of the Hertzsprung–Russell diagram.

An example of a red giant is Aldebaran (in the constellation of Taurus). Betelgeuse (the bright red star in Orion) is a supergiant with an estimated diameter 800 times that of the Sun, sufficient to fit in the Solar System out beyond the orbit of Mars!

Fig 9.1 shows the comparative sizes of the Sun as it is now and as a red giant. The effect of this transition on our Solar System will be dramatic. The increased luminosity will vaporise the inner planets in the Solar System, whilst the outer planets, such as Jupiter and Saturn, will lose their frozen gaseous outer layers to reveal rocky cores.

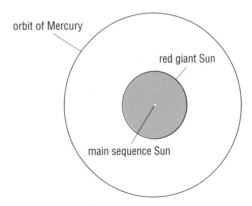

Fig 9.1 The Sun as it is now and as it may be as a red giant.

| QUESTION | **9.1** When our Sun becomes a red giant, it may swell out, so that its diameter is 30 times its present value. Its temperature may fall from 5800 K to 4000 K. Use Stefan's law to show that it will shine with a brightness (luminosity) approximately 200 times its present value. |

Energy production in a red giant

The core of a red giant star can reach temperatures of 100 million kelvins. This is enough for helium nuclei to fuse. (This requires higher temperatures than hydrogen fusion, because the nuclei are more highly charged.) So helium burning is the principle energy release mechanism in red giants, with carbon being formed by the **tri-alpha process**. Two helium nuclei fuse to form beryllium:

$$^4\text{He} + {}^4\text{He} \rightarrow {}^8\text{Be} + \gamma$$

This then fuses with a third helium nucleus to form carbon:

$$^8\text{Be} + {}^4\text{He} \rightarrow {}^{12}\text{C} + \gamma$$

In some cases helium also combines with the carbon to form oxygen:

$$^{12}\text{C} + {}^4\text{He} \rightarrow {}^{16}\text{O} + \gamma$$

One consequence of this is that carbon and oxygen are the most common elements in the Universe, after hydrogen and helium.

With such prodigious energy production, mass loss is substantial. In addition, large amounts of matter are lost from the star's outer layers where its gravitational field is weak. Red giants can have an annual mass loss of $1 \times 10^{-7} \times M_\odot$, compared with the Sun's annual mass loss of $1 \times 10^{-14} \times M_\odot$ ($M_\odot = 1$ solar mass).

The structure of a $5M_\odot$ red giant is shown in Fig 9.2. Notice that the active helium core and hydrogen fusion shell make up a minute part of the structure. Most of the star is made up of a low-density envelope.

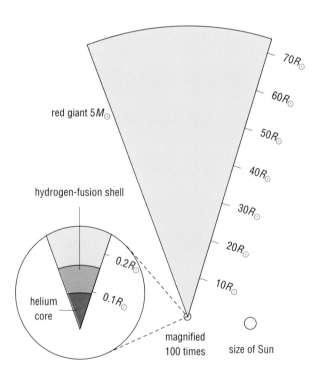

Fig 9.2 Cross-section of a red giant star; notice that the helium core and its surrounding hydrogen shell occupy only a tiny fraction of its volume.

Fusing heavier elements

Elements heavier than carbon can be formed if conditions of temperature and pressure are sufficiently extreme. However, since gravity is so important in converting gravitational potential energy to thermal energy, only the most massive stars are capable of fusing elements such as neon, oxygen and silicon. Such stars have an onion-like structure, as shown in Fig 9.3. Table 9.1 outlines the fusion reactions in massive stars.

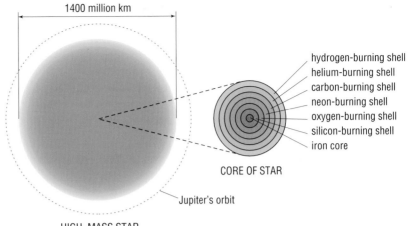

Fig 9.3 Fusion shells in an old, high-mass star.

Table 9.1   The products of nuclear fusion in main-sequence and red giant stars

Nuclear fuel	Nuclear products	Minimum ignition temperature/K	Mass needed/$M_{\odot}$	Duration of fusion in a $25M_{\odot}$ star
H	He	4×10^6	0.1	7×10^6 years
He	C, O	120×10^6	0.4	0.5×10^6 years
C	Ne, Na, Mg, O	600×10^6	4	600 years
Ne	O, Mg	1.2×10^9	8	1 year
O	Si, S, P	1.5×10^9	8	0.5 year
Si	Ni to Fe	2.7×10^9	8	1 day

Notice that iron is the heaviest element that can be formed by the processes of fusion described above. Iron is the most stable of all nuclei; if it is to fuse to form heavier elements, an input of energy is required. However, heavier elements are formed in the iron-rich core of stars with masses in excess of eight solar masses ($8M_{\odot}$). This is part of the instability that triggers a supernova. In a supernova, a star explodes, and conditions may become sufficiently extreme for iron to fuse and produce very heavy elements. These heavy elements can then undergo fission to produce lighter elements.

9.2 THE DEATH OF STARS

Gravity triumphant

Eventually red giant stars fail to undergo further fusion reactions. They have not run out of fuel, but gravitational pressure is insufficient to initiate further fusion reactions. So what happens at this point? The life-long battle between gravity and the outward expansive pressure due to thermal energy (sometimes known as **hydrostatic pressure**) comes to an end, with gravity triumphant. The star collapses, its fate depending on its mass. The more massive the star, the more spectacular is the finale. There are four possible outcomes, which are discussed below.

Red, white and black dwarfs

Red dwarfs are very-low-mass stars (less than 40% that of the Sun), which are very cool. As they are so small, the principal heat flow mechanism is convection, which allows almost all of the hydrogen fuel to be fused. These stars therefore 'burn' for a long time, although the internal temperature is

Fig 9.4 shows the relative abundances of the chemical elements in the Solar System. Note that the scale is logarithmic, so that hydrogen is approximately 10^{12} times as abundant as the least abundant elements such as tantalum.

Use your knowledge of the composition of stars and of stellar fusion processes to explain this graph. Try to explain the following points:

- Hydrogen and helium are the most common elements in the Solar System. (Where are they?)
- Carbon and oxygen are the next most common elements.
- Iron is more common than its near neighbours.
- The heaviest elements are the least common.
- The graph zig-zags up and down, so that elements with an even number of protons (and neutrons) are more common than their neighbouring elements with an odd number of protons.

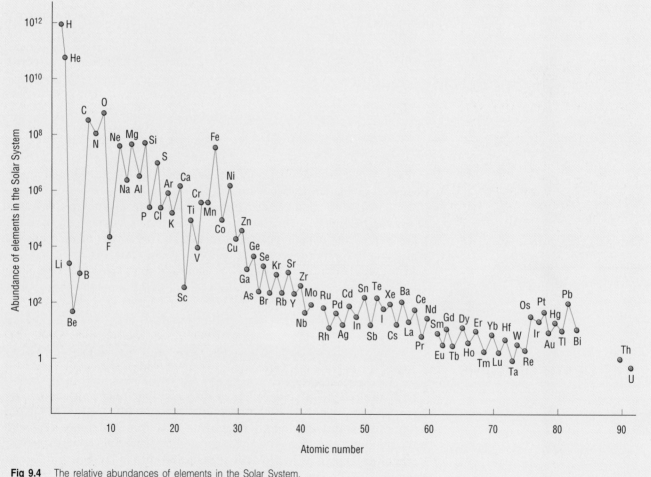

Fig 9.4 The relative abundances of elements in the Solar System.

never sufficient to ignite helium fusion. Eventually, when hydrogen fusion finishes, the star collapses under the force of gravity, to become a white dwarf (at the bottom left-hand corner of the Hertzsprung–Russell diagram). The temperature is pushed up by the contraction, but there is no further fuel available. The outer layers are lost into space, and the core of closely packed helium nuclei remains. It occupies a volume similar to that of the Earth. The star eventually fades to become a black dwarf, an inert lump in space.

Sun-like stars

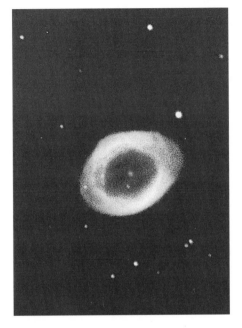

Fig 9.5   A planetary nebula, the Ring Nebula, observed in the constellation of Lyra.

After fusing hydrogen during their time on the main sequence, stars between 0.4 and 8 solar masses become red giants. However, owing to their relatively small mass (if 2×10^{30} kg can be referred to as small!), they cannot provide sufficient gravitational contraction to generate a core temperature high enough to fuse carbon and oxygen into heavier elements. However, the contraction and renewed core fusion can ignite the helium in the shells around the nucleus, causing the outer layers of the red giant to balloon outwards.

The star is now doing two things, contracting at the core and expanding in the outer layers. **Radiation pressure** (the outward pressure due to the radiation being produced) from the centre is sufficient to push the outer layers from the star to form a so-called **planetary nebula**. (This term is misleading as it has nothing to do with planets, other than that 19th-century astronomers felt that the nebulae looked like planets when viewed through a telescope.) A photograph of such a nebula is shown in Fig 9.5.

The expanding gases and dust particles are illuminated by the intense ultraviolet radiation from the star at the centre. Typically, stars may lose 50% of their mass in this process.

The final inward-collapsing remnant of a star will keep on contracting due to gravity until a new equilibrium is reached, when the electrons refuse to pack into a smaller volume. This is a quantum-mechanical effect, known as **electron degeneracy**. According to the Pauli exclusion principle, there is a limit to the number of electrons that can exist in a given energy level. When fusion ceases, the star collapses due to gravitation to reach this high-density limit.

At this stage, gravitational potential energy lost in the collapse is turned into thermal energy, which explains why the star glows white hot. It has become a white dwarf. A star the size of our Sun will contract to a size similar to the Earth, with the ejection of a planetary nebula. Without a further energy source, the white dwarf is effectively doomed. As it radiates its energy into space, it becomes cooler and fainter, until it becomes a black dwarf. Since a white dwarf is so dense, it takes billions of years for all the heat to escape from the interior and be lost.

The more massive a white dwarf, the smaller it will be, since the gravitational forces are stronger. This leads to a maximum mass of 1.4 solar masses for a white dwarf. This is known as the **Chandrasekhar limit**, after the astronomer who discovered it.

More massive stars

As discussed earlier, a high-mass star is capable of producing higher temperatures at its core and so it can fuse heavier elements. At 600 million kelvins in a star of four solar masses ($4M_\odot$), carbon will fuse, whilst for increasingly heavier stars, neon and oxygen will fuse. Ultimately, a star of eight solar masses is capable of fusing silicon to form iron. However, iron will not fuse owing to its nuclear stability. At the cessation of fusion, the star reaches a crisis. The core ceases to generate energy, although the layers just outside the core will sustain fusion for a short period of time.

The entire energy-producing region is about the size of the Earth, while the star has a volume sufficient to encompass Jupiter's orbit. The electrons in the stellar centre are effectively propping up the weight of a massive star. Eventually, when the core exceeds 1.4 solar masses (the Chandrasekhar limit), the electrons cannot support this huge weight. Instead of having a white dwarf at the centre, the core collapses further. At this point the density of the core in a star of 25 solar masses may exceed $1 \times 10^{12} \, \mathrm{kg \, m^{-3}}$. Electrons start to combine with protons in the nucleus to form neutrons. Neutrinos are also released:

$$e^- + p \rightarrow n + \nu$$

In less than a second the core density escalates to $4 \times 10^{17} \, \mathrm{kg \, m^{-3}}$. The core is effectively made up mostly of neutrons, compressed to nuclear density. It has become a **neutron star**. Matter is virtually incompressible at this density, and the collapse stops. However, the outer layers are plunging inwards at huge speeds (up to 15% of the speed of light), only to collide with this exceedingly dense core. Huge pressures and temperatures result, causing the falling material to bounce back, powered in part by the flood of neutrinos. After a few hours the shock wave reaches the surface, tearing it away in a huge explosion, known as a **supernova**. This process may cause the ejection of as much as 95% of the mass of a 25 solar mass star.

The story of the supernova SN1987a

Two early examples of supernovae observed from the Earth are the Crab Nebula and Tycho's star, whose explosions were first seen in 1054 and 1572 respectively. The remnants of these explosions are still visible as expanding gas clouds. The Crab explosion actually occurred 6500 years earlier; its light had taken that long to reach the Earth. Nevertheless the 'Guest star' (as it was known) managed to outshine the planet Venus, and for a while could be seen in broad daylight.

We do not often observe supernovae occurring in our galaxy, or in its immediate vicinity. So astronomers were very fortunate to witness a supernova 160 000 light-years away in the Large Magellanic Cloud, a satellite galaxy of our own – see Fig 9.6. The discovery was made in 1987 by the Canadian astronomer Ian Shelton (Fig 9.7). The doomed star SK 69202 had been catalogued and studied by Nicholas Sanduleak. It was a 20 solar mass giant, with a luminosity 10 000 times that of the Sun. The supernova was catalogued as SN1987a.

The supernova raised the star's magnitude from 12 to 3, an increase in luminosity of a factor of 4000. Theory suggests that 0.1 s after core collapse the neutrino luminosity would have a value of 10^{47} W, compared to the optical (light) luminosity of 10^{45} W of the rest of the observable Universe. For a fraction of a second supernova SN1987a outshone the rest of the Universe by a factor of 100!

Theoretical astronomers predicted that there should have been a burst of neutrinos prior to this optical observation. The hunt was on. Records

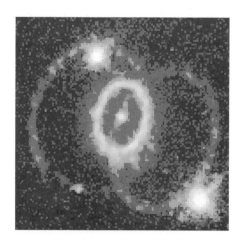

Fig 9.6   The supernova 1987a, in the Large Magellanic Cloud, as viewed by the Hubble Space Telescope.

Fig 9.7 Ian Shelton, the astronomer who first spotted supernova SN1987a, with his telescope.

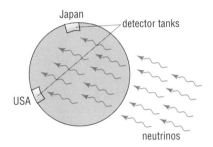

Fig 9.8 Neutrinos from supernova 1987a passed through the Earth before being detected in Japan and the USA.

Fig 9.9 Jocelyn Bell Burnell, discoverer of pulsars, and now Professor of Physics at the Open University.

from neutrino detectors in Japan and the USA were examined, and sure enough 3 h before the light arrived there was a surge in the number of neutrinos. Not only did this verify our theories on supernovae, it also reinforced the fact that neutrinos travel at speeds close to the speed of light and pass easily through solid matter. Japan and the USA both lie in the Northern Hemisphere (Fig 9.8), and the neutrinos must have penetrated the detecting tanks from the bottom, after passing through the Earth.

Pulsars

In the event of a supernova, most of the material of a dying star is flung out into space. What happens to the small, dense core that remains?

One of the most unusual celestial observations was made by Jocelyn Bell, a graduate student at Cambridge University, in November 1967 (Fig 9.9). She discovered a mysterious radio source, which pulsed with a highly regular period of 1.337 301 19 s. As it was thought that the signal always came from the same part of the sky, it was not of terrestrial origin. It was thought that the signals might be from an extra-terrestrial civilisation, and this led to the code name LGM (for 'Little Green Men'). However, within a period of weeks three more similar sources had been found, and it was clear that the objects were natural, and the term **pulsar** was adopted.

So what is a pulsar? A pulsar is a rotating neutron star. The pulsing light is actually a lighthouse-like beam being emitted as the star rotates. When the main-sequence star collapses, it spins faster and faster, rather like an ice-skater who brings her arms in when spinning. The magnetic field also becomes more intense (of the order of a billion times). The combination of these two effects is to concentrate the radiation into narrow beams emanating from the magnetic poles – see Fig 9.10. If the Earth is in the line of these beams as they sweep round, pulses of radiation are detected.

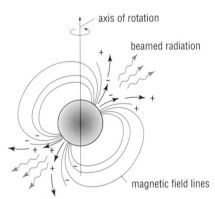

Fig 9.10 Pulsars are thought to be rotating neutron stars, which emit beams of radiation, like a lighthouse.

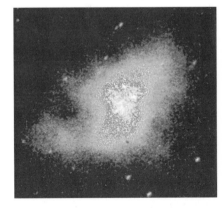

Fig 9.11 There is a pulsar at the centre of the Crab nebula.

In October 1968 a pulsar was found in the Crab Nebula – see Fig 9.11. This was the vital link in confirming that a pulsar is a rotating neutron star, as theory had suggested that a neutron star would be at the heart of the Crab Nebula. Fig 9.12 shows how the intensity of the radio signal varies with time.

Although the physics of neutron stars may be remarkable, there is a further possibility for the most massive stars. This is the formation of a black hole, which is discussed in the next section.

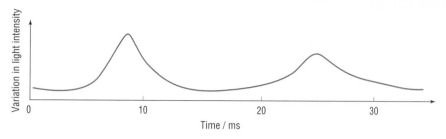

Fig 9.12 The Crab nebula pulsar can be seen pulsing with a period of 33 ms. Two pulses are detected during each cycle, as its two beams of unequal intensity sweep over the Earth.

9.4 BLACK HOLES

What is a black hole?

Black holes are sometimes thought of as a recent idea in cosmology. However, the idea of their existence can be traced back nearly 200 years to the eminent French mathematician Pierre Simon, Marquis de Laplace. In 1796, Laplace speculated that, according to Newtonian theory, a star with a sufficiently large gravitational field would bend its light back and therefore appear dark. It was not until after the publication of Einstein's general theory of relativity that the American physicist John Wheeler named such objects **black holes**.

To understand why light cannot escape from a black hole, we need to use the concept of **escape velocity**. If you throw a stone upwards from the surface of the Earth, it will come back down again. The faster it is moving when it leaves your hand (or the faster it is 'fired' from some sort of 'gun'), the higher it will rise before it starts to fall. If it is fired very fast indeed (so that it leaves the gun vertically at 11 km s^{-1}), it will have enough energy to escape from the Earth's gravity, and it will not fall back down. So the escape velocity is the upward velocity that a body must have to escape from a gravitational field.

We can calculate the escape velocity for an object of mass m on the surface of a planet of mass M and radius R, by equating its kinetic energy at the planet's surface with the gain in gravitational energy it experiences as it escapes:

$$\frac{1}{2} mv^2 = \frac{GMm}{R}$$

so

$$v^2 = \frac{2GM}{R}$$

What has this to do with black holes? Picture a star collapsing. As it contracts, its density increases, and as a consequence the escape velocity at its surface increases. Eventually, if the star becomes small enough (and hence dense enough), the escape velocity may equal the speed of light. Any further contraction will result in all light and matter being trapped inside, unable to escape. The star is surrounded by an **event horizon**, a boundary beyond which we cannot see any event. The radius of the event horizon is usually referred to as the **Schwarzschild radius** (named after the astronomer Karl Schwarzschild, who carried out a great deal of work on the subject). The Schwarzschild radius (R_{Sch}) can be calculated from the formula:

$$R_{Sch} = \frac{2GM}{c^2}$$

where G is the universal gravitational constant, M is the mass of the star and c is the speed of light. This comes from the equation above for escape velocity, in which c has been substituted for v, and the equation rearranged. (Strictly speaking, general relativity should be taken into account when deducing this result.)

QUESTIONS	**9.4** Show how the equation for escape velocity can be used to deduce the equation for the Schwarzschild radius.
	9.5 Suppose that 2×10^{31} kg (10 solar masses) of matter from a dying star collapsed to form a black hole.
	(a) Calculate its Schwarzschild radius.
	(b) Calculate its density.

When does a black hole form?

For a black hole to form, a dense stellar core with a mass greater than about two solar masses is needed. Of course, this may have come from a much more massive star, the outer layers having been lost in the violent explosion of a supernova.

Once this matter has collapsed under its own gravity to a radius less than the Schwarzschild radius, what happens? Theory suggests that it keeps on collapsing. It shrinks and shrinks, until it is no more than a point in space, referred to as a **singularity**.

Neutron stars, which are not massive enough to become black holes, are very compressed. However, their shrinking is stopped by **neutron degeneracy**. This is a rule which says that there is a limit to the number of neutrons that can occupy any energy level, and once the neutrons have filled up the lowest energy levels, the neutron star stops collapsing. (This is equivalent to electron degeneracy, discussed above.) In the case of a black hole, however, the gravitational attraction is strong enough even to overcome this effect.

| QUESTIONS | **9.6** At the end of its life, could the Sun become a black hole? |
| | **9.7** Consider a collapsing star that has a mass equal to five solar masses (10^{31} kg) in a sphere 20 km across. Would this be a black hole? |

Detecting black holes

Since we know that black holes emit no light, it may seem that we could never detect them. However, detection *is* possible. One opportunity for detection is offered by a black hole that is part of a binary system. Matter that falls into a black hole becomes very hot, and as a consequence it emits X-rays. If the black hole were an isolated star, the rate at which matter is sucked in would be very small, and the intensity of the X-rays emitted would be small. However, if the black hole is part of a binary star system, then matter can be drawn from the partner star, producing an accretion disc, which emits high-intensity X-rays – see Fig 9.13.

Fig 9.13 An artist's impression of a black hole that is part of a binary star system. The black hole attracts matter from the star, to form an accretion disc. As the matter falls into the black hole, X-rays are generated.

Fig 9.14 Cygnus X-1 is believed to contain a black hole.

Strong X-ray sources were identified using the Uhuru satellite in the early 1970s. If the X-ray emission fluctuates due to the eclipsing of binary stars (the time period for the eclipse can be as short as 10 ms), the finite speed of electromagnetic radiation can be used to deduce the size of the source. Additionally the Doppler shift (see section 7.5) of light from the visible star can provide sufficient evidence to allow the calculation of the masses of both members of the binary system. With the masses and volumes known, it is possible to speculate as to whether the invisible star is a black hole. Stars that provide the strongest evidence are Cygnus X-1 (Fig 9.14) and HDE 226868.

Gravitational lensing

The gravitational field of a black hole is so strong that even light is affected. Light is deflected as it passes near a black hole. (The deflection of light in a gravitational field was first predicted by Albert Einstein in his general theory of relativity.) Fig 9.15 shows what happens to light from a distant star if a black hole lies in its path as the light travels to the Earth.

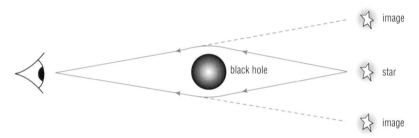

Fig 9.15 Gravitational lensing by a black hole. Light rays from a distant star are bent as they pass through the black hole's gravitational field. The result is two or more images of the same star.

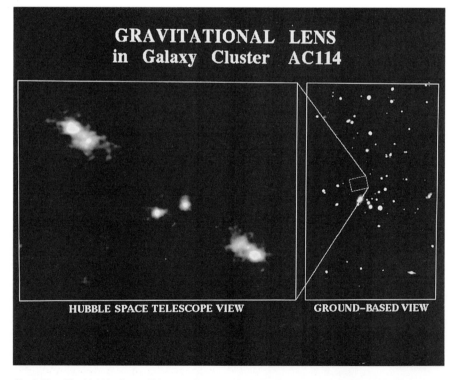

Fig 9.16 The Hubble Space Telescope has provided double images of distant stars. These double images are thought to arise due to gravitational lensing by a black hole.

HOW STARS DIE

Rays from the star pass on either side of the black hole. They are attracted by its strong gravity, and deflected towards an observer on the Earth. The observer sees two images of the star. The black hole acts as a **gravitational lens**.

To date, no gravitational lenses have been found in our galaxy; however, several have been discovered far from our galaxy. These involve remote luminous quasars (see section 10.5). The Hubble Space Telescope has provided photographs of some examples, one of which is shown in Fig 9.16.

INVESTIGATION

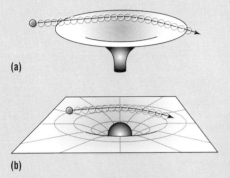

Fig 9.17 Two demonstrations of 'gravitational lensing'.

Here are two ways to represent the effect of a black hole on the path of light from the stars:

1. Use the $1/r$ hill (commonly used for the Rutherford scattering demonstration) in an *inverted* position to produce a two-dimensional analogy. Roll a ball-bearing at the hill so that it passes to one side of the centre – see Fig 9.17(a). Find out how the deflection of the ball changes if you roll it along different paths.

    The ball represents light; the inverted hill represents the gravitational field of a black hole. A ray of light is deflected towards a black hole, just as the ball is deflected towards the inverted hill.

2. A similar effect can be achieved by using a thin rubber sheet weighted in the middle. Again, a ball-bearing is propelled either side of the centre – see Fig 9.17(b).

QUESTION

9.8 A gravitational lens causes us to see two images of a distant star. What evidence would you look for to check that the images are of the same object and not of similar but different objects?

SUMMARY ASSIGNMENT

Summarise what you have learnt about the fate of stars by copying and completing Table 9.2.

Table 9.2

Mass of main-sequence star	Elements produced by fusion	Ultimate fate of star
mass < $0.4M_\odot$		
$0.4M_\odot$ < mass < $1.4M_\odot$		
$1.4M_\odot$ < mass < $8M_\odot$		
mass > $8M_\odot$		

SUMMARY

The mass of a star determines its lifetime in the main sequence.

The mass of a star determines the elements that are produced by fusion.

The mass of a star determines its ultimate fate.

Chapter 10

GALAXIES AND QUASARS

So far, we have only considered the stars in the night sky. However, stars are part of larger structures, namely galaxies. This chapter explores what we know about galaxies, as well as looking at quasars, remote objects that we do not as yet fully understand.

LEARNING OBJECTIVES

After studying this chapter you should be able to:

1. describe the structure of galaxies;

2. explain how galaxies differ;

3. calculate the orbital speed of a star in a galaxy;

4. describe the properties of a quasar;

5. suggest a possible energy mechanism for a quasar.

10.1 THE MILKY WAY

Our galaxy

On a clear moonless night away from city lights, the Milky Way can be seen as a faint hazy band stretching across the whole night sky. Its existence has been known since ancient times. However, the idea that the Milky Way was a 'star system' had to wait until Galileo made an observation of the sky with a telescope. He saw that the Milky Way was composed of countless dim stars, as shown in Fig 10.1.

Fig 10.1 A wide-angle photo of the Milky Way.

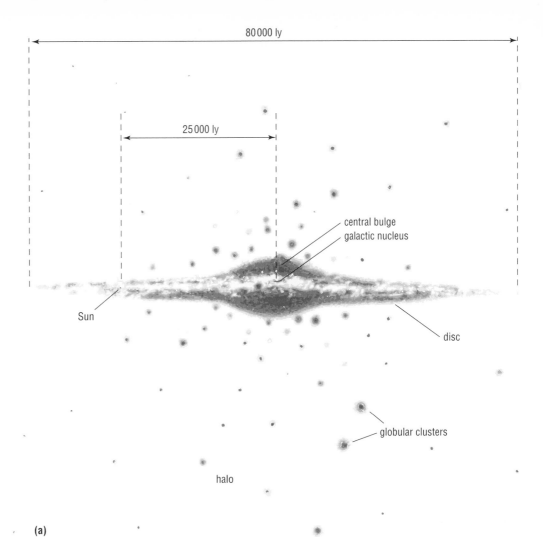

80 000 ly

25 000 ly

central bulge
galactic nucleus

Sun

disc

globular clusters

halo

(a)

Perseus arm

rotation

Sun

Orion arm

Cygnus arm

Centaurus arm

Sagittarius arm

(b)

Fig 10.2 The Milky Way galaxy, showing the
position of the Solar System: **(a)** side
view; **(b)** plan view.

The Milky Way is a galaxy that contains around 200 billion stars. It has a disc shape, with a central spherical bulge, so that it resembles a spinning catherine wheel when seen from above. Fig 10.2 shows two views of the galaxy, with the position of the Solar System marked. When we look towards the centre of the galaxy, we see a dense ribbon of stars across the sky.

The galaxy is, of course, vast – almost 100 000 ly across. But don't forget that this is small compared to the Universe, which is probably more than 10 000 million light-years across.

Observations show that there are many spiral galaxies. The Andromeda spiral (catalogued as M31) is the nearest spiral galaxy, at a distance of 2.2 million light-years. Its distance has been determined by observation of Cepheid variables. The galaxy is just visible to the unaided eye in the southern sky.

So if you are ever asked how far you can see with the naked eye, the answer is a remarkable 2.2 million light-years (around 13×10^{18} miles), a lot further than most people might have thought!

The labelling M31 (Messier 31) for the Andromeda spiral comes from a list of just over 100 non-stellar objects catalogued by the French astronomer Charles Messier. His aim in compiling this list was to provide a catalogue of objects to ignore when looking for comets! Other famous objects in this list include the Crab Nebula (M1) and the Orion Nebula (M42).

QUESTION

10.1 On the scale of Fig 10.2(a), how far away would the Andromeda spiral be?

What's in our galaxy?

There are three major components of our galaxy:

- A thin disc
- A central bulge
- A halo

The halo consists of stars and globular clusters but very little dust or gas. There are no young bright stars, which suggests that the halo contains most of the oldest stars in the galaxy. The **globular clusters** contain between 100 000 and 1 000 000 stars crowded into a region 10–30 pc (33–100 ly) across. Fig 10.3 shows such a cluster.

It is the age of stars (10–15 billion years) in globular clusters that fixes the age of our galaxy at a minimum of 15 billion years. It is reasonable to assume that all the stars in a cluster were formed at the same time, from the collapse of a single gas cloud. With the passage of time, stars reach the end of their main-sequence lives, those of lower mass being later to leave the main sequence owing to their slower evolution. So if we find a cluster containing low-mass stars, we can estimate the age of the cluster.

The bulge at the centre of our galaxy is also crowded. However, there is evidence that it contains hot young stars, unlike the halo. This evidence is difficult to collect as, in addition to the densely packed stars, the galactic centre contains many dust clouds, making visual observation impossible. Most of our data come from infrared and radio observations.

Fig 10.3   A globular cluster; these typically contain up to a million stars.

Try to see M31, the Andromeda spiral galaxy. The sketch map in Fig 10.4 shows you how to find it. (The task is made easier if you have a planisphere.) You will need to be well away from street-lights, as M31 has a magnitude of 4.8, making it fairly faint to the naked eye. (Recall that the faintest objects visible to the naked eye have magnitude 6.)

Once you have found it, see if you can then observe it with binoculars or a telescope. You should be able to see its spiral shape – see Fig 10.5.

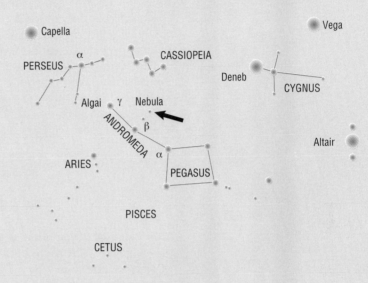

Fig 10.4   Finding the Andromeda spiral galaxy.

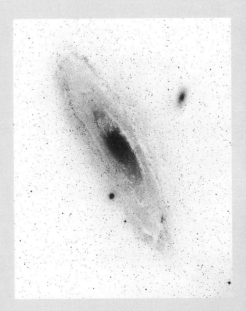

Fig 10.5   The Andromeda spiral galaxy, M31.

10.2 Using the information in the previous paragraphs, calculate the average separation between stars in a globular cluster. Would the inhabitants of a planet orbiting one of the stars in a globular cluster have darkness at night?

10.2 THE ROTATION OF GALAXIES

Fast movers

The Sun with its Solar System is moving through space at half a million miles per hour, because our galaxy is rotating. If the galaxy did not rotate, it would collapse under its own gravitational attraction. Galaxies do not rotate as solid objects; instead, they show differential rotation, with stars nearer the galactic centre moving the quickest, as shown in Fig 10.6.

The Sun's speed of half a million miles per hour (230 km s⁻¹) was deduced by using Doppler shifts of 21 cm radio-wave radiation from hydrogen gas within the spiral arms of our galaxy. Since we know the Solar System's distance r (25 000 ly) from the galactic centre and its speed v through space, we can calculate the orbital period T from

$$T = \frac{2\pi r}{v} = \frac{2\pi \times 25\,000 \times 9.46 \times 10^{15}\ \text{m}}{230\,000\ \text{m s}^{-1}}$$

$$= 6.5 \times 10^{15}\ \text{s} = 2.0 \times 10^{8}\ \text{years}$$

This value of 200 million years for one rotation emphasises the vast size of our galaxy. The same data also can be used to work out a value for the mass M of our galaxy by using Kepler's third law, represented by the relationship (see section 2.3):

$$T^2 = \frac{4\pi^2 r^3}{GM}$$

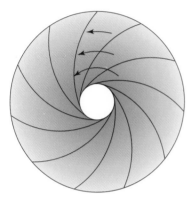

Fig 10.6 The rotation of a galaxy; the length of the arrows represents the speed of rotation at different points along the spiral arms.

10.3 Astronomers have observed many spiral galaxies. Some are seen 'edge-on', like the view of the Milky Way in Fig 10.2(a). By focusing their telescopes on different parts of the spiral, they can examine the light coming from parts of the galaxy that are moving towards us, and parts that are moving away. Their motion can be detected by the Doppler shift of lines in their spectra. For a spiral galaxy seen edge-on, which regions would show:

(a) the greatest frequency increase (blue-shift);

(b) the greatest frequency decrease (red-shift);

(c) no Doppler shift in spectral frequencies?

(d) Sketch a graph to show how the frequency varies across the diameter of the galaxy.

10.4 Use the data given above in the text to show that the mass of our galaxy must be of the order of 9.3×10^{10} solar masses.

[mass of the Sun = 2.0×10^{30} kg]

10.3 CLASSIFYING GALAXIES

Spirals and ellipses

Not all galaxies are spirals like our Milky Way galaxy and the M31 Andromeda galaxy.

Galaxies can be classified into three main classes, i.e. **elliptical**, **spiral** and **irregular**, according to their shapes, with these forms being subdivided according to fine detail. Fig 10.7 shows two examples of elliptical galaxies. Fig 10.8 and Table 10.1 show a classification scheme invented by Edwin Hubble.

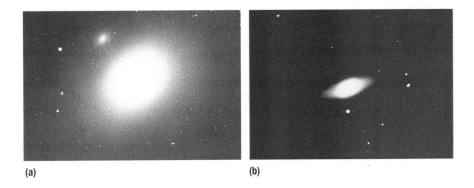

Fig 10.7   Two elliptical galaxies: **(a)** type E3 and **(b)** type E7.

(a)   (b)

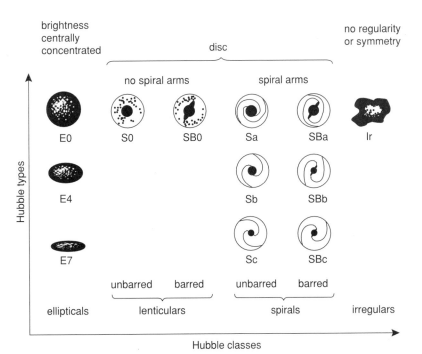

Fig 10.8   Hubble's classification of galaxies.

Table 10.1   Classification of galaxies

Spiral galaxies	There are straightforward spirals and there are barred galaxies. Both types can be classified further by the relative size of the central bulge
Elliptical galaxies	The elliptical galaxies are classified from E0 (circular) to E7 (highly elliptical) according to their outline, and seem to contain mainly older stars
Irregular galaxies	The Magellanic Clouds that orbit our galaxy are irregular, with no apparent organisation in their structure

Galactic clusters

The nearest galactic neighbours to our Milky Way galaxy are the irregular forms of the Large and Small Magellanic Clouds. The Large Magellanic Cloud lies at a distance of 160 000 ly. Beyond this there are around twenty other galaxies within a 2 500 000 ly radius, and these make up the local **cluster**. The most significant member of this cluster is the Andromeda galaxy, with its orbital companions. The Andromeda galaxy is larger than our own, with a mass of 300 000 million solar masses (200 000 for our Milky Way galaxy).

Fig 10.9 shows the positions of the galaxies in our local cluster. Note that most of the minor galaxies orbit either our Milky Way galaxy or the Andromeda galaxy.

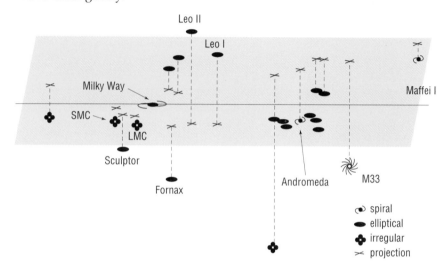

Fig 10.9 Our local cluster of galaxies. Our galaxy is the Milky Way. LMC and SMC are the Large and Small Magellanic Clouds.

The Virgo cluster shown in Fig 10.10 is at a distance of 50 million light-years. It has over 1000 galaxies in a region 7 million light-years across. The three biggest galaxies in the photograph have diameters of the order of 2 million light-years (25 times that of our galaxy). There are bigger clusters than this, some with over 10 000 galaxies.

If all this seems remarkable, clusters are grouped into **superclusters**. Tens of clusters make up these enormous assemblies, which may be spread over a distance of 100 million light-years. Superclusters are filamentary, leaving vast voids of empty space in between.

Fig 10.10 Part of the Virgo cluster of galaxies.

QUESTION

10.5 What force is responsible for the clustering together of galaxies?

GALAXIES AND QUASARS

ASSIGNMENT

Fig 10.11 lists five elliptical galaxies. They are arranged in order of increasing distance. The position of a particular spectral line is indicated in each spectrum, together with its red-shifted wavelength. The normal wavelength of the prominent line H is 396.8 nm.

10.6 Use the red-shift equation

$$\frac{\Delta \lambda}{\lambda} = \frac{v}{c}$$

to calculate the recessional velocity of each galaxy. [Give your answer to two significant figures.]

10.7 Now use Hubble's law

$$v = H_0 d$$

to calculate the distance to each galaxy. Assume $H_0 = 50$ km s^{-1} Mpc^{-1} and 1 pc = 3.26 ly. [Give your answer in millions of light-years.]

10.8 Plot a graph of observed wavelength against distance, and comment on it.

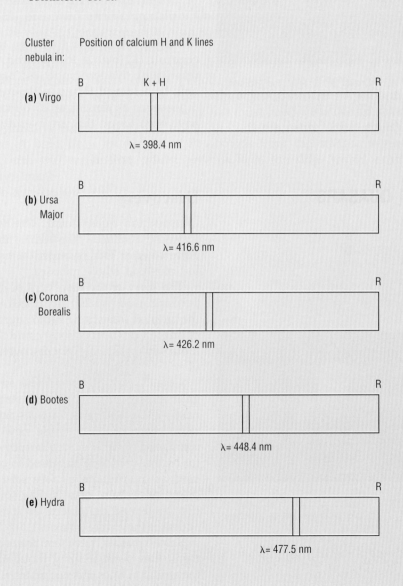

Cluster nebula in:

Position of calcium H and K lines

(a) Virgo
λ = 398.4 nm

(b) Ursa Major
λ = 416.6 nm

(c) Corona Borealis
λ = 426.2 nm

(d) Bootes
λ = 448.4 nm

(e) Hydra
λ = 477.5 nm

Fig 10.11 The red-shift in the spectral lines of distant galaxies. The lines indicate the position of calcium H and K lines.

Black holes and quasars

Astronomers can only speculate on the answer to this question. Quasars are relatively small, and, for quasars to give out more light than many galaxies, the power source must be very powerful indeed. Only one type of object fits these criteria – a black hole! A hint of this came from studying **active galaxies**, galaxies that seem to be intermediate between ordinary galaxies and quasars. Quite often these have jets issuing from them, as do a good number of quasars. They are also usually very active in the radio spectrum.

So how can a black hole, which 'sucks in' light, be the mechanism for the objects that give out the most light? The theory proposes that some galaxies may have **supermassive black holes** at their centres. These may have a mass of between 10^6 and 10^9 solar masses. Such a massive black hole cannibalises any nearby matter at the rate of 10 solar masses a year.

Using powerful computers, scientists have been able to model conditions around such a black hole. They found that such a dense flow of matter into the black hole could set up outward forces, which in turn would set up jets of matter moving at relativistic speeds through the accretion disc. This is shown in Fig 10.16. How this appears to us depends on our viewpoint.

From the side, we see a radio galaxy; closer to the line of the jet, we see a quasar; and if we look directly along the jet, we see a **blasar** (this is an extremely luminous galactic object, with a quasar-like centre).

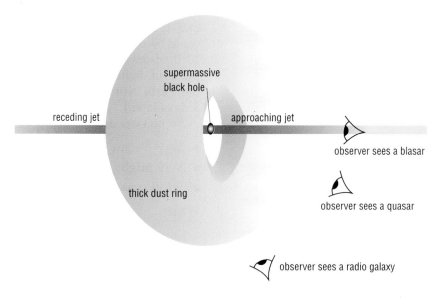

Fig 10.16 The black hole model of a quasar.

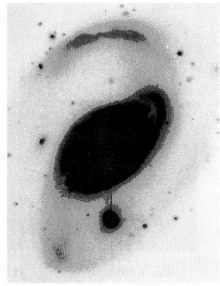

Fig 10.17 Optical image of the spiral galaxy NGC4319 and the quasar Markarian 205 (small circular object at bottom). The quasar is very distant, and the unrelated galaxy is in the line of sight.

Could quasars be closer?

Many astronomers are sceptical about the use of red-shift to determine the distance to quasars. Accepting that objects are receding from us at $0.9c$ takes some believing. Photographs have been taken of quasars that seem to be linked to nearer galaxies, although these may not be genuine links, but rather line-of-sight images (Fig 10.17).

However, no one has been able to provide much evidence for a local hypothesis, particularly as no quasars have been found with blue-shifts, which would be expected from local motions. Quasars still provide us with more questions than answers.

GALAXIES AND QUASARS

10.9 A galaxy may contain 10^{11} stars. Each star transforms 1 part in 10^{14} of its mass into energy each year. A black hole at the heart of a quasar may consume 10^9 stars each year. Use this information to show that a quasar may be as bright as 10^{12} galaxies.

10.10 Fig 10.16 shows how a quasar may appear as a radio source, a quasar or a blasar, depending on the position from which it is viewed. If astronomers search the sky for these objects, would you expect them to find more radio sources, quasars or blasars?

10.6 THE MOST DISTANT OBJECTS

Farther and farther

As quasars appear to be the most distant heavenly bodies, it might be interesting to look at how the 'distance record' has increased over the years. Tables 10.2 and 10.3 show how the visible Universe has expanded since Bessel first measured the distance of a star beyond the Solar System.

Table 10.2   Distant objects, determined by parallax and Cepheid variables

Estimated distance /light-years	Object	Distance measurement technique	Astronomer	Year
6 (modern value 11)	61 Cygni	parallax	Bessel	1838
20 (modern value 26)	Vega	parallax	Struve	1840
200		limit for parallax		1900
900 000 (modern value 2150 000)	Galaxy M31	Cepheids	Hubble	1924

Table 10.3   Distant objects, determined by red-shift

Distance /millions of light-years	Speed of recession (% of c)	Object	Astronomer	Year
200	1.4	galaxy NGC7619	Humason	1928
2 100	15	galaxy Ursa Major 2	Humason/ Hubble	1936
4 600	32.6	cluster 1448		1956
5 100	36.2	3C295	Minkowski	1960
5 700	41	quasar 3C147	Schmidt	1964
11 200	80.1	quasar 3C9	Schmidt	1965
13 100	93.4	quasar 0051 279	Warren	1987

It is worth noting that the eminent 18th-century astronomer William Herschel proposed that other galaxies lay outside our Milky Way galaxy. He had no means of measuring the distances. As each different technique was introduced, the distances underwent a significant leap.

Edwin Hubble's name is evident in the use of both Cepheids and red-shifts. This underlines his contribution to the fields of astronomy and cosmology. It is the Hubble constant that is used to determine astronomical distances from measurements of the recessional velocity.

Is there a limit? Clearly, yes. A distant galaxy would cease to be visible if its recessional velocity were equal to c. This occurs at a distance of about 15 000 million light-years (1.32×10^{23} km). This would suggest that the Universe is 15 000 million years old, something that will be discussed in the next chapter. So the most distant quasar, known as 0051 279 and at a distance of 13 100 million light-years, is almost at the limit of the observable Universe. Furthermore, we are seeing it as it was soon after the Big Bang. An observer close to this quasar and looking towards us would fail to see our Sun (even if the technology were available) as our Solar System would not have formed at the time light would have set off!

SUMMARY

Galaxies are structures that contain billions of stars.

Galaxies can be classified into spirals, ellipses and irregular structures.

Galaxies are found in clusters.

The most distant galaxies are moving away from us at relativistic speeds.

Quasars are very luminous star-like objects at immense distances.

Quasars may be powered by supermassive black holes.

Chapter 11

COSMOLOGY

We have discussed the history of astronomy, some of the methods used by astronomers, and some of their observations. However, we have not yet examined what are perhaps the biggest questions of all: How did the Universe come into being, how has it evolved, and how might it end? Attempts to answer these questions form the study of cosmology. In this chapter, we will look at how some of the evidence presented in earlier chapters has contributed to modern ideas of the history of the Universe.

LEARNING OBJECTIVES

After studying this chapter you should be able to:

1. apply Hubble's law to models of the Universe;

2. interpret Olbers' paradox to explain why it suggests that the model of an infinite, static Universe is incorrect;

3. understand what is meant by the 'cosmological principle';

4. describe, and explain the significance of, the microwave background radiation;

5. understand the Big Bang model of the Universe;

6. describe the evolution of the Universe;

7. understand that the Universe may be open, flat or closed depending on its density.

11.1 WHY IS THE SKY DARK AT NIGHT?

Fig 11.1 Stand in a crowd and, no matter in which direction you look (horizontally), there will be someone in your line of sight.

Olbers' paradox

We all know that it is dark at night. But just why is this? On the face of it, this may seem a daft question. However, it was this question that undermined Newton's idea of an infinite, static Universe.

The problem is this: Newton imagined that the Universe was infinitely large, and that it was unchanging over long periods of time. Thus there must be an infinite number of stars spread out through this infinite space. If this were a correct model of the Universe, it was suggested that the night sky should be as bright as day, if not brighter.

To understand this, picture yourself standing in a large crowd of people. If you look in any horizontal direction, you will find that you are looking at another person, as shown in Fig 11.1. Now if the Earth is in a Universe that extends to infinity, then no matter in which direction you look in the night sky, you ought to see a star. We ought to be receiving starlight from all directions, and therefore the night sky should be as bright as a star's surface. This is shown in Fig 11.2.

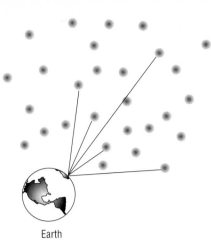

Earth

Fig 11.2 Olbers' paradox: in an infinite and static Universe, no matter in which direction you look, there will be a star in your line of sight.

This problem is known as Olbers' paradox, since it was publicised in 1826 by Heinrich Olbers. However, the original idea was not his. Thomas Digges, as long ago as 1576, and later Johannes Kepler, in 1610, had both discussed the problem. Kepler did not see it as a paradox, since he believed the Universe to be finite; whereas Olbers assumed that clouds of matter absorbed the radiation from more distant stars. However, the latter still poses a problem, as the cloud would heat up until it glowed as brightly as a star.

Incidentally, for a Universe in equilibrium, the 'line-of-sight' problem suggests that the night sky should glow as brightly as a star (and so should the daytime sky). It also suggests a hot Universe with everything heated to the temperature of stellar surfaces. So the paradox could also be stated as: 'Why is the Universe so cold?'

QUESTION

11.1 Olbers' paradox starts from the assumption that the Universe is static (unchanging) and infinite. It concludes that the sky would be uniformly bright.
  (a) If this were the case, what would happen to the Earth's temperature?
  (b) The light from distant stars is faint, because it spreads out. (Think of the inverse square law.) So we might expect some areas of the sky to be less bright than others. Use the idea that there are more distant stars than nearby stars to explain why this is not the case.
  (c) Think about the assumptions involved in Olbers' paradox. Which of these might be incorrect? What evidence is there to support your suggestions?

Challenging assumptions

Present-day cosmologists believe that they understand why the sky is dark. Olbers' paradox is based on incorrect assumptions. The Universe is neither static nor infinitely old, as Olbers had assumed.

As we saw in the last chapter, the galaxies are all moving apart. The more distant a galaxy is, the faster it is receding from us. This is deduced from the red-shifts of light coming from the stars. What effect does the red-shift have on the light that reaches us from distant stars? We will think about light of wavelength λ and frequency f. We can think of the light as consisting of photons of energy E. These quantities are related by the equation

$$E = hf = hc/\lambda$$

where h is Planck's constant. A red-shift increases the wavelength and reduces the frequency. This has the effect of reducing the energy of photons. Furthermore, the rate of arrival of photons will be less than the rate from a static source, since each photon from the receding source has a longer distance to travel than the previous photon. So the recession of the galaxies results in less energy reaching us from them.

In 1848 the author Edgar Allan Poe (Fig 11.3) proposed another explanation for the darkness of the night sky, based on the age of the Universe.

Fig 11.3 Edgar Allan Poe, author of the first detective stories, also made a contribution to our understanding of the Universe.

COSMOLOGY

He stated that the night sky is dark as it is not infinitely old. Light from the most distant stars has not yet had time to reach us.

In fact, to explain the dark night sky, we must assume that the Universe is both finite and expanding.

QUESTION   11.2 Suggest why both the above conditions are necessary if the night sky is to be dark.

11.2 THE COSMOLOGICAL PRINCIPLE

Three assumptions

Consideration of Olbers' paradox leads us to try to establish a more accurate description of the Universe. To do this, we start by making three assumptions, which are together known as the **cosmological principle**. These assumptions are homogeneity, isotropy and universality:

- **Homogeneity** This is the assumption that matter is evenly distributed throughout the Universe. Clearly, this is not true on a small scale, as planets, stars and galaxies exist. However, on the largest scales, this does become more correct, despite the observation of superclusters of galaxies and theories suggesting a 'lumpy' Universe.

- **Isotropy** This is the assumption that the Universe is the same in all directions. Again, this is not true on a small scale, but more true on a large scale.

- **Universality** This states that all the physical laws that we know on the Earth apply equally everywhere else in the Universe. This appears to be the case; for example, the spectra of atoms in distant galaxies are the same as those of atoms of the same elements on Earth.

One way to understand the cosmological principle is to realise that it suggests that there is nothing special about our position in the Universe. The Earth is just an ordinary planet orbiting an ordinary star in an ordinary galaxy. If we were on another planet in another galaxy, the Universe would look just the same.

One consequence of this is that we deduce that the Universe has no edge or centre, since these would be 'special' places.

QUESTION   11.3 Explain which of the assumptions of the cosmological principle would break down if we could stand at the 'edge' of the Universe.

The expanding Universe

Here is a useful analogy that can help us to visualise an expanding Universe. We picture a balloon being blown up, as shown in Fig 11.4. If we represent galaxies as coins stuck on the surface of the balloon, we

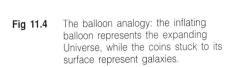
Fig 11.4   The balloon analogy: the inflating balloon represents the expanding Universe, while the coins stuck to its surface represent galaxies.

---

notice that, as the balloon is inflated, the distance between 'galaxies' increases. (Note that the *surface* of the balloon represents the *volume* of the Universe.)

What are the strengths of this analogy?

- The more distant coins are moving away faster than the nearer ones, in accordance with the Hubble law.

- There is no central point; no matter which coin you choose all others are moving away from it.

- The surface of the balloon has no centre or edge, in accordance with the cosmological principle. All points on its surface are equivalent to one another.

- The history of the Universe can be represented by the expansion of the balloon. Later, if we let the air out, the balloon may shrink. Perhaps this is the fate that will befall the Universe.

Note that this suggests that the Universe may be of limited size and yet have no edge, just as the surface of a balloon or a ball is finite but has no edge. This provides an answer to a commonly asked question: 'What is beyond the Universe?' The Universe may be finite but have no edge; there is no 'beyond'.

At this point, we should remind ourselves of the relationship between Hubble's law and the age of the Universe. Recall that the red-shift of distant galaxies increases with their distance. This is not so much because the galaxies are moving away from us; rather, the space between us and them is expanding. To distinguish between Doppler shifts (where an object moves through space) and this red-shift, where an object may remain stationary in expanding space, we use the term **cosmological red-shift**.

In Chapter 7, we saw that the Hubble constant H_0 is given by

$$H_0 = \frac{\text{speed of recession}}{\text{distance}} = \frac{v}{d}$$

and the age of the Universe can be estimated to be $1/H_0$.

So if we know the value of the Hubble constant H_0, we can calculate the age of the Universe. However, as mentioned earlier, Hubble's constant is not known precisely owing to the difficulty in measuring large distances by an independent method. Currently accepted values are between 50 and 100 km s^{-1} Mpc^{-1}.

Assuming $H_0 = 50$ km s^{-1} Mpc^{-1}, and given that 1 Mpc = 3.1×10^{22} m, we have

$$\text{age of Universe} = \frac{3.1 \times 10^{22} \text{ m}}{50\,000 \text{ m s}^{-1}}$$

$$= 6.2 \times 10^{17} \text{ s}$$

$$= 20\,000 \text{ million years}$$

This is older than the age of any known stars, which suggests that it is a realistic estimate.

QUESTION

11.4 Use the maximum value for H_0 to deduce a minimum estimate for the age of the Universe suggested by using Hubble's law.

Starting from a singularity

Referring back to the balloon analogy of the history of the Universe, we can see that the model suggests that, at some time in the past, the Universe had no volume. This is the starting point of the theory of the Big Bang, which is now the most generally accepted scientific model of the origin of the Universe.

The Big Bang model suggests that all matter and space was concentrated in zero volume, a **singularity**. At this time the Universe was at an infinitely high temperature, and had infinitely high density. Since then, the Universe has expanded and cooled to form galaxies and stars. A couple of points are worth noting. The Big Bang did not occur at a specific place but rather it filled the whole Universe. Furthermore, time can be considered to have started with the Big Bang. There was no 'before the Big Bang'.

So what evidence is there to support the Big Bang theory? And how has the Universe evolved since that event?

Primordial background radiation

As long ago as 1948 George Gamow suggested that the early stages of the Universe must have been very hot and therefore the Universe should still contain large amounts of black-body radiation (see Chapter 6). A year later, Ralph Hermann and Robert Herman pointed out that the expansion of the Universe would cause the wavelength of this radiation to lengthen, suggesting that the radiation's temperature would have decreased since the Big Bang. Its wavelength would be in the radio-wave region of the electromagnetic spectrum. However, radio-astronomy was in its infancy at this time, so it wasn't until 1960 that Robert Dicke of Princeton University suggested that this 'Big Bang radiation' might be detected. The search was on.

Ironically, the radiation was detected by accident in 1965, just a few miles away from Princeton, by two scientists who weren't even looking for it! Arno Penzias and Robert Wilson of Bell Telephone Laboratories were testing a new microwave horn antenna at Holmdel, New Jersey, for use in telecommunications – see Fig 11.5. They had a problem; no matter in which direction they turned the horn, they detected unwanted background noise. They tried cooling the circuitry to reduce electrical noise, and they tried cleaning dirt from the horn (mainly the accumulation of bird droppings!). None of this had any effect. Moreover, the same noise was detected in all directions, suggesting that it did not come from a source on Earth. It was only by a chance conversation with a colleague that the two scientists learnt of Dicke's work, and came to realise they had detected the 'echo' of the Big Bang.

The energetic, short-wavelength radiation from the time of the Big Bang had been red-shifted until it had become low-energy, long-wavelength microwaves. Measurements of the peak wavelength suggested that the temperature of the radiation was approximately 3 K. A detailed study by the Cosmic Background Explorer (COBE) satellite, launched by NASA in 1989, has since confirmed this.

Fig 11.5 Arno Allan Penzias and Robert Wilson with the horn antenna with which they first detected the microwave background radiation.

| QUESTION | 11.5 Accurate measurements of the spectrum of the Universe's background radiation show that it matches that of a black body whose temperature is 2.735 K. Use Wien's displacement law (see section 6.1) to calculate the wavelength at which the spectrum peaks, and show that this appears in the radio-wave region of the electromagnetic spectrum. |

11.4 THE HISTORY OF THE UNIVERSE

The hot past

What follows is a brief outline of the physical conditions that are thought to have existed in the Universe, from the moment of the Big Bang to the present day. The diagram shown in Fig 11.6 provides a good idea of the stages involved.

In the early instants of the life of the Universe (first two shells), temperatures were exceedingly high. All of the matter and energy (particles and photons) were compressed into a tiny volume. Such a high concentration of energy meant that matter was broken down into its most fundamental units. Subsequently, as the Universe expanded, it cooled, and eventually particles were able to combine to form, first, protons and neutrons (fourth shell), and then atoms (fifth shell), and finally molecules. In the seventh shell, stars are born and heavy elements are formed by fusion in them. Finally, life evolved.

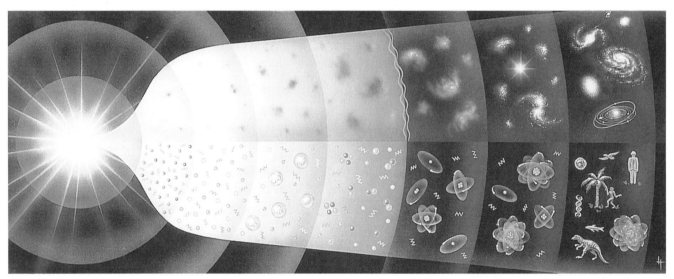

Fig 11.6 An artist's impression of the history of the Universe since the Big Bang. The shells are explained briefly in the text.

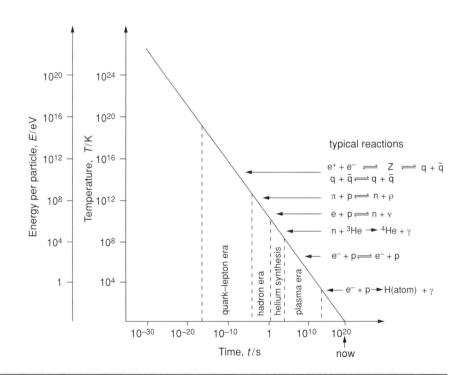

Fig 11.7 The history of the Universe; this graph shows how its temperature has decreased since the Big Bang.

COSMOLOGY

Fig 11.7 shows a schematic diagram of this cooling. Notice that the diagram is split into eras, which we will look at individually. The vertical axis has two scales: temperature, and average energy per particle. To get a feel for this energy scale, it may help you to recall that 13.6 eV (electronvolts) is the energy required to remove the electron from the proton in a hydrogen atom, in the process known as ionisation. Therefore, if the average energy per particle is more than 13.6 eV, we would not expect to find atomic hydrogen. On this basis we can deduce the particles that existed at various times.

The quark–lepton era

Quarks and leptons are among the fundamental particles of Nature. Protons and neutrons are made of **quarks**; electrons and neutrinos are examples of **leptons** (light-weight particles). Our knowledge of the quark–lepton era is based on the study of high-energy particle physics experiments carried out at CERN and elsewhere, using particle accelerators. These machines are capable of energies of 100 GeV (10^{11} eV). Using results from these experiments, the following events are thought to have occurred. Between 10^{-16} s and 10^{-5} s after the Big Bang, the Universe was very hot, with the temperature dropping from 10^{20} to 10^{12} K. This is much hotter than the temperatures found in the centres of stars at any stage of their development. The typical energy per particle decreased from 10^{16} to 10^8 eV. In these conditions there would have been a high density of leptons – such as electrons, positrons (anti-electrons) and neutrinos – and of quarks. These would interact vigorously, but the temperature was still too high for protons or neutrons to be formed. For this reason, this phase is named the quark–lepton era.

Note that we have little experimental evidence to support this picture of the first fraction of a second of the life of the Universe. This is because of the difficulty of achieving such high energies in a laboratory experiment.

The hadron era

As the temperature decreased to 10^{12} K, the energy per particle decreased to 200 MeV, which is sufficient for the strong nuclear forces between quarks to take effect. Groups of quarks joined together to form protons and neutrons (hadrons), amongst other particles.

Towards the end of this era, as the energy and temperature continued to fall, the existing protons and neutrons became more stable. Eventually, this set a limit to the proton/neutron ratio that still exists in the Universe today. As the neutron is slightly heavier, it makes up a smaller share of the number. The ratio is five protons for each neutron.

Helium synthesis

At temperatures where the particles had energies around 0.15 MeV, deuterons could be formed from the fusion of a proton and a neutron:

$$n + p \rightarrow {}^2H + \gamma$$

This in turn led to the formation of helium nuclei by the following reactions:

$${}^2H + {}^2H \rightarrow {}^3H + p$$

$${}^3H + {}^2H \rightarrow {}^4He + n$$

At the same time, a tiny amount of lithium, the third element in the Periodic Table, was formed.

After this time, 25% of the mass of the Universe was in the form of helium nuclei. The calculation of the hydrogen/helium ratio is important, as the result is found to agree with observations. This is a strong piece of evidence to support the Big Bang theory!

By this time, the temperature had fallen too far for any possibility that fusion might produce the nuclei of heavier elements. These had to wait for the appearance of stars, and the processes of stellar evolution described earlier in Chapters 8 and 9.

The plasma era

Very little changed after the first three minutes, until the Universe was 500 000 years old, with a temperature of 4000 K. During this time, as the name suggests, matter was in the form of a plasma, in which electrons, protons, helium nuclei and photons were all separate. At 4000 K hydrogen atoms formed, a typical reaction in this era being:

$$e^- + p \rightarrow {}^1H + \gamma$$

This simply represents the process by which a proton collected an electron to become a hydrogen atom.

SUMMARY ASSIGNMENT

Figs 11.6 and 11.7 show the evolution of the Universe after the Big Bang. Summarise this information in a table, using the following headings:

- Time from Big Bang/s
- Temperature/K
- Energy per particle/eV
- Key features

QUESTION

11.6 You may wonder how scientists can determine temperatures in the past. The relationship between temperature T and time t is approximately $T^2 t = 10^{20}$ K^2 s. Check this relationship by selecting four points from the graph shown in Fig 11.7. Tabulate their values of T, t and $T^2 t$, and show that the value of the last quantity is constant.

11.5 THE FUTURE OF THE UNIVERSE

From Big Bang to Big Crunch?

Will the Universe ever come to an end? We cannot be sure; the inconclusiveness of the answer is linked to our uncertainty of the age of the Universe. We picture the Universe expanding outwards after the Big Bang. Will it continue to expand for ever, or will gravity pull it back in on itself, so that it will end in a 'Big Crunch'?

To decide between these two possibilities, we need to know the density of matter in the Universe. If there is enough matter in the Universe, its density will be sufficiently high for it to collapse back in on itself, since there is a gravitational attraction between all matter.

To understand these two possibilities, we will consider an analogous situation: 'firing' a projectile upwards from the Earth's surface. At first, the projectile has kinetic energy. As it rises, it slows down because it is doing work against gravity. Now there are two possibilities: If its initial kinetic energy is sufficient then it will escape from the gravitational influence of the planet. If its kinetic energy is insufficient, eventually the projectile will stop and the kinetic energy will be regained as the projectile falls back down. So how does this relate to the fate of the Universe?

The fate of the Universe depends on its mass. If there is sufficient gravitational attraction, the expansion of the Universe, which we observe, will stop and matter will be pulled back again. However, if the Universe's mass is less, its gravity will be too weak, and its expansion may slow down but never stop, rather like a projectile that has surpassed the required escape velocity of a planet. There is a boundary between these two fates, where gravity is neither 'too much' nor 'too little'. Thus there is a **critical density**, analogous to a velocity equal to the escape velocity, where the Universe's expansion is slowed down but never quite stops until an infinite time has passed.

So there are three possible outcomes, as shown in Fig 11.8:

- The Universe is **closed** – its density is sufficiently high that its gravity is strong enough to pull everything back to a Big Crunch.
- The Universe is **open** – its density is low, so that gravity is too weak to stop it from expanding forever.
- The Universe is **flat** – its density has the critical value, so that, in principle, it will only start to contract after an infinite time.

In Fig 11.8, you can also see how the Universe would continue to expand if there was no gravity to slow down its expansion.

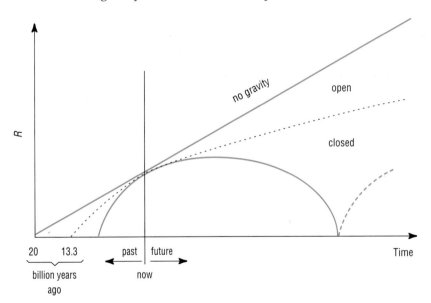

Fig 11.8 The radius R of the Universe has increased since the Big Bang. In future, it may continue to increase for ever, or the Universe may start to contract.

So, in which Universe do we live? You can see from Fig 11.8 that, if we knew how old the Universe is, we could decide which curve we are on. However, we have already discussed the difficulties in obtaining an accurate value for the Hubble constant, which is the quantity we need to know to calculate the age of the Universe. In fact, we saw earlier (section 7.4 and question 7.9) that the age of the Universe is somewhere between 10 billion and 20 billion years; from Fig 11.8, you can see that the boundary between open and closed Universes falls in this range.

If we knew the density of the Universe, we could work out the strength of its gravitational attraction, and hence know its fate. However, it is no easy task to determine the amount of matter in a given volume of space.

Naturally, assumptions need to be made; observing visible matter is hard enough, and cosmologists believe that dark matter (such as planets, low-temperature gas clouds, etc.) may make up 90% of the mass of the Universe. Indeed, it may be the case that the mass of neutrinos may be significant. Neutrinos have only a tiny mass, perhaps only 1/10 000th of the mass of an electron, but the vast number of neutrinos in the Universe could make this an important consideration.

Estimates of the density of matter in the Universe show that it is close (within a factor of 10) to the calculated critical density. Some theorists believe that there are reasons to suppose that we do, in fact, live in a Universe that has the critical density. This would be a very special Universe indeed, a 'flat' Universe with exactly the minimum mass required if it is to go on expanding forever.

QUESTION

11.7 What is the fate of a closed Universe? What happens after the Big Crunch? Fig 11.8 hints at one possibility. What do you think is meant by a 'bouncing' Universe?

11.6 CALCULATING THE CRITICAL DENSITY

The great escape

If the Universe has a density equal to the critical density ρ_0, then each galaxy is moving just fast enough to escape from the gravitational pull of the rest of the Universe. Its velocity is equal to the escape velocity, according to the projectile analogy discussed above.

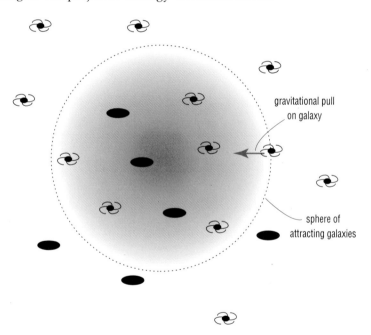

gravitational pull on galaxy

sphere of attracting galaxies

Fig 11.9 A distant galaxy experiences the gravitational pull of all the matter within the sphere shown here.

We will consider a galaxy at a distance r from the Earth, as shown in Fig 11.9. It is receding from us with velocity v, equal to the escape velocity. It is pulled back by the mass M of all the matter in the sphere of radius r, in the same way that a projectile launched from the surface of the Earth is pulled back by the mass of the Earth.

The mass of matter in this sphere depends on the density of matter in the Universe, ρ_0. Since the volume of a sphere is $(4/3)\pi r^3$, we can write

$$M = \frac{4}{3}\pi r^3 \times \rho_0$$

The escape velocity v is given by

$$v = \sqrt{\frac{2GM}{r}} \quad \text{or} \quad v^2 = \frac{2GM}{r}$$

But the galaxy's velocity is also given by Hubble's law:

$$v = H_0 r \quad \text{or} \quad v^2 = H_0^2 r^2$$

where H_0 is the Hubble constant. Eliminating v, substituting for M, and rearranging gives

$$\rho_0 = \frac{3H_0^2}{8\pi G}$$

Now you can see why it is important to know an accurate value for the Hubble constant. Without it, we cannot calculate the critical density accurately, and so we cannot tell whether we live in an open, closed or flat Universe.

Note that relativity is needed to derive this relationship correctly, although the final result is the same.

The value of ρ_0

The value of H_0 lies in the range 50–100 km s^{-1} Mpc^{-1}. We take the higher value and change to SI units (1 Mpc = 3.1 × 10^{22} m). Thus H_0 = 100 km s^{-1} Mpc^{-1} becomes H_0 = 100 × 10^3 m s^{-1}/(3.1 × 10^{22} m) = 3.26 × 10^{-18} m s^{-1} m^{-1}. So substituting in the equation for ρ_0 gives

$$\rho_0 = \frac{3 \times (3.26 \times 10^{-18})^2}{8\pi \times 6.67 \times 10^{-11}}$$

$$= 1.9 \times 10^{-26} \text{ kg m}^{-3}$$

This density corresponds to only a few hydrogen atoms per cubic metre; of course, on Earth we are used to densities of the order of 1000 kg m^{-3}, but there is a lot of almost empty space in between the planets, stars and galaxies.

QUESTIONS

11.8 (a) Use the lower value for H_0 to calculate a lower limit for the value of ρ_0.

(b) For these two calculated values of ρ_0, estimate the critical density in terms of an average number of hydrogen atoms per cubic metre.
[mass of hydrogen atom = 1.7 × 10^{-27} kg]

(c) Current evidence suggests that the average density of the Universe is of the order of three hydrogen atoms per cubic metre. Does this fall in the range of critical densities calculated above? What consequences does this have for predictions of the future of the Universe?

11.9 Fig 11.10 shows how the size of the Universe changes for open and closed models, as well as for a Universe without gravity. By observing the spectra of stars, and measuring red-shifts and blue-shifts, astronomers can detect the motion of distant galaxies. What would you expect astronomers to observe for stars at different distances in the three models at times t_1, t_2 and t_3?

Would it ever be possible for some stars to exhibit red-shifts whilst others in the same sky show blue-shifts? If so, explain how and when it would occur.

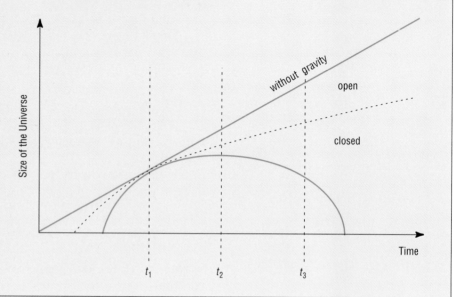

Fig 11.10 Possible fates of the Universe (see question 11.9).

SUMMARY

Olbers' paradox suggested that, if Newton's static and infinite model of the Universe was correct, the night sky would not be dark. The Universe is therefore finite and expanding.

The cosmological principle states that the Universe is homogeneous, isotropic and universal.

The Big Bang model is the favoured scientific model of the origin of the Universe. Evidence in support of this includes the 3 K microwave radiation, the relative abundance of hydrogen and helium, and the greater red-shifts of distant objects.

The 3 K microwave radiation was originally emitted at short wavelengths, which were subsequently stretched as the Universe expanded.

The Hubble constant can be used to determine the age of the Universe:

$$\text{age} = \frac{1}{H_0}$$

The Universe may be open, closed or flat. The fate of the Universe depends on gravitational attraction. We are unable to determine which model is correct as it is not known whether the Universe's density is more than or less than the critical density ρ_0.

The critical density is related to the Hubble constant and the universal gravitational constant:

$$\rho_0 = \frac{3H_0^2}{8\pi G}$$

EXAMINATION QUESTIONS: Theme 3

T3.1

(a) The Sun produces energy by nuclear fusion, where hydrogen is converted into helium. This could be represented by the equation:

hydrogen → helium + positrons + neutrinos + energy

(i) Name the product of the reaction which is *anti-matter*.

(ii) Name the particle of matter which corresponds to the anti-matter product which you named in (a) (i).

(iii) For each 1.000 kg of hydrogen involved in the fusion reaction, the rest mass of the products is only 0.993 kg. The change in mass is associated with the production of energy. Calculate the energy produced from 1.000 kg of hydrogen.

(iv) Calculate the rate of loss of mass of the Sun if the Sun's power output is 3.9×10^{26} W.

(b) Cosmologists have speculated that our Sun will use hydrogen as a principal energy source for 1.0×10^{10} years. Calculate the total mass loss from the Sun due to fusion during this time. Assume that there are 365 days in a year.

(c) Fusion in our Sun occurs not only with hydrogen but also with heavier elements. Discuss whether it is possible for a star to have an infinite life by fusion of elements having ever-increasing mass number.

(d) Fusion is not the principal mechanism by which a star loses mass.

(i) Suggest alternative mechanisms for this mass loss.

(ii) Describe the stages in the life of the star at which the rate of mass loss is greatest.

(UCLES December 1993)

T3.2

The evolution of a star can be mapped out on a Hertzsprung–Russell (H–R) diagram.

(a) Describe the lifetime of a star of 1 solar mass from its formation to its final state. Your answer should include:

(i) a sketch of the H–R diagram,

(ii) a line on your H–R diagram mapping the star's evolution,

(iii) the physics of each stage of development, together with the energy processes involved,

(iv) the position of our Sun on the H–R diagram.

(b) Comment on how your answer to (a) (iii) would differ for stars of mass 3 solar masses and of mass 10 solar masses.

(UCLES June 1992)

T3.3

Our Sun will never become a neutron star since, for this event to occur, a mass of greater than 1.4 solar masses is required.

(a) Since our Sun will not become a neutron star, what will be its eventual fate?

(b) Why is a neutron star so named?

(c) Explain why a mass greater than 1.4 solar masses is required if a neutron star is to be formed.

(d) (i) From what type of star does a neutron star evolve?

   (ii) Outline the process of formation of a neutron star.

(e) A hydrogen atom has a diameter of approximately 10^{-10} m and its nucleus is of diameter approximately 10^{-15} m. Comment on the suggestion that a neutron star consists of collapsed atoms.

(UCLES June 1992)

T3.4

Recent theories suggest that the lifetime T of some stars may be calculated by comparing the mass m of the star with that of the Sun. It is suggested that T and m are linked by the equation:

$$T_{star}/T_{Sun} = m_{Sun}/m_{star}$$

(a) Assuming this relationship, calculate the lifetimes of **two** stars of 0.1 and 10 solar masses. Your answers should be relative to the lifetime T_{Sun} of the Sun.

(b) Assuming the age of the Sun is 5×10^9 years, which places it half-way through its lifetime, calculate the lifetimes of the two stars in (a).

(c) Outline how the **three** stars (the Sun and the 0.1 and 10 solar mass stars) compare in their evolution and behaviour *after* their existence on the main sequence.

(UCLES June 1994)

T3.5

(a) Astronomers interested in a nearby star made the following measurements.

   (i) The wavelength at which the intensity–wavelength graph for the star peaks.

   (ii) The electromagnetic energy arriving at the Earth's surface from the star per second per unit area normal to the direction of the star.

   (iii) The distance of the star from the Earth.

   Explain how this information enables them to calculate the surface temperature of the star and its luminosity L.
   How does this data, when collected together from a large number of stars, lead to the concept of a *main sequence star*?

(b) Describe the helium production process by which the energy radiated from a star is generated. Explain why this process takes place only in regions of very high temperature.
   How do you account for the high temperatures generated within stellar masses before this main energy-releasing process can begin?

(c) Some stars evolve into *white dwarfs*, others into *red giants*. Explain the terms printed in *italic*.

   Explain briefly what decides the state into which a star evolves when it leaves the main sequence.

(ULEAC 1996 Specimen Paper)

T3.6

Describe and explain the formation and properties of the following cosmic objects:

(a) planetary nebulae,

(b) neutron stars,

(c) pulsars,

(d) white dwarfs.

(UCLES December 1992)

T3.7

Many of the objects which we see in the sky are binary stars. A binary star consists of two stars rotating about a common centre of mass.

(a) What evidence would lead you to believe that two neighbouring stars were part of a binary system rather than two stars with a wide separation in approximately the same line of sight?

(b) One of the stars in a binary system is thought to be a 'black hole'. What evidence would support this suggestion?

(c) The separation of two stars in a particular binary system is 1.0×10^{10} m with the centre of mass of the system 9.0×10^9 m from the visible star. The visible star has mass 1.0×10^{30} kg. The other star is a black hole of mass M.

   (i) Draw a sketch of the binary system, incorporating the above data.

   (ii) Suggest a reason why the mass M of the black hole is of the order 9×10^{30} kg.

   (iii) Calculate the density ρ of the black hole, given that

   $$\rho = \frac{c^6}{4.2G^3M^2}$$

   where c is the speed of light in a vacuum.

   (iv) Comment on your answer to (c)(iii) in relation to your knowledge of black holes.

(UCLES June 1992)

T3.8

(a) In adopting the Big Bang model of the Universe the terms

   (i) open

   (ii) flat, and

   (iii) closed

   are used. Explain with the aid of diagrams how two-dimensional and three-dimensional worlds can exist which are open (unbounded) and closed (bounded).

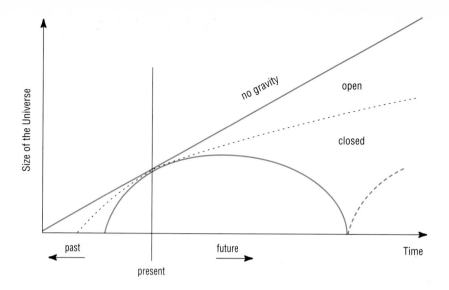

Fig T3.8 Diagram for question T3.8.

(b) It is possible to calculate the age of the Universe because the expansion of the Universe is a function of time, as shown in Fig T3.8. Discuss the evidence required for an accurate determination of the age of the Universe.

(UCLES June 1993)

T3.9

Write an article on black holes which would be suitable for popular readership. Your article should include:

(a) an understanding of the term 'black hole',

(b) the conditions under which black holes are formed,

(c) an account of how some laws of physics apply to such condensed matter,

(d) the effect on an object placed in the vicinity of a black hole.

(UCLES December 1992)

Appendix A

USEFUL DATA

Physical constants

Quantity	Symbol	Value	Unit
speed of light *in vacuo*	c	3.00×10^8	m s^{-1}
permeability of free space	μ_0	$4\pi \times 10^{-7}$	H m^{-1}
permittivity of free space	ε_0	8.85×10^{-12}	F m^{-1}
charge of electron	e	1.60×10^{-19}	C
Planck constant	h	6.63×10^{-34}	J s
gravitational constant	G	6.67×10^{-11}	$\text{N m}^2\,\text{kg}^{-2}$
Hubble constant	H_0	$50\text{–}100$	$\text{km s}^{-1}\,\text{Mpc}^{-1}$
Boltzmann constant	k	1.38×10^{-23}	J K^{-1}
Stefan constant	σ	5.67×10^{-8}	$\text{W m}^{-2}\,\text{K}^{-4}$
Wien constant	α	2.90×10^{-3}	m K
electron rest mass	m_e	9.11×10^{-31}	kg
proton rest mass	m_p	1.67×10^{-27}	kg
neutron rest mass	m_n	1.67×10^{-27}	kg

Astronomical bodies

Body	Mass/kg	Mean radius/m
Sun	2.00×10^{30}	7.00×10^8
Earth	6.00×10^{24}	6.38×10^6
Moon	7.35×10^{22}	1.74×10^6

Solar luminosity $L_\odot = 3.83 \times 10^{26}\ \text{W}$

Units of distance

1 astronomical unit (AU) $= 1.50 \times 10^{11}\ \text{m}$
1 parsec (pc) $= 206\,265\ \text{AU} = 3.08 \times 10^{16}\ \text{m} = 3.26\ \text{ly}$
1 light-year (ly) $= 9.45 \times 10^{15}\ \text{m}$

Approximate light travel times

Sun to Earth	8.31 minutes
Sun to Pluto	4.46 hours
Sun to nearest star	4.2 years
Across our Galaxy	1×10^5 years
To Andromeda (M31)	2.2×10^6 years
To edge of observable Universe	1.5×10^{10} years

The planets

Planet	Mass/kg	Radius/m	Orbital radius/m	Orbital period
Mercury	3.3×10^{23}	2.4×10^6	5.8×10^{10}	87.97 d
Venus	4.9×10^{24}	6.1×10^6	1.1×10^{11}	224.7 d
Earth	6.0×10^{24}	6.4×10^6	1.5×10^{11}	365.26 d
Mars	6.4×10^{23}	3.4×10^6	2.3×10^{11}	687 d
Jupiter	1.9×10^{27}	7.1×10^7	7.8×10^{11}	11.86 y
Saturn	5.7×10^{26}	6.0×10^7	1.5×10^{12}	29.46 y
Uranus	8.7×10^{25}	2.4×10^7	2.9×10^{12}	84.01 y
Neptune	1.0×10^{26}	2.2×10^7	4.5×10^{12}	164.79 y
Pluto	1.3×10^{22}	1.1×10^6	5.9×10^{12}	248.54 y

(d = days, y = years)

Appendix B

MATHEMATICAL DERIVATIONS

B.1 TIME DILATION IN SPECIAL RELATIVITY

To an outside observer, time seems to run more slowly for a moving object. We say that time is dilated. (This is explained in section 3.3.)

Following Fig 3.10, we can see that observer B sees light travel up and down once in the carriage. For B, the light travels distance $2l$, and it takes time $t_0 = 2l/c$. Hence

$$l = \frac{t_0 c}{2} \tag{B.1}$$

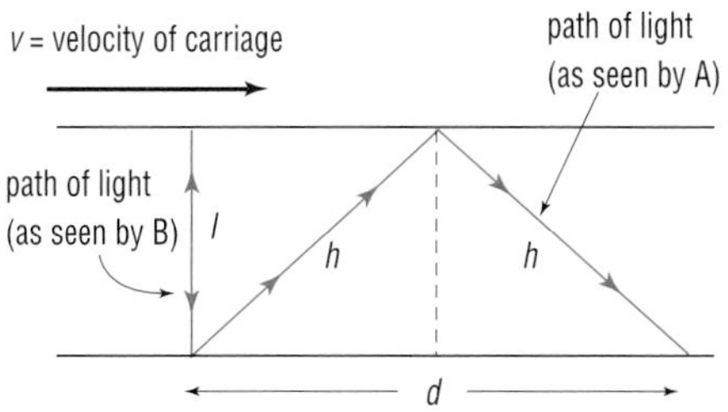

To the external observer A, the light travels a longer path. It travels distance $2h$, and it takes time $t = 2h/c$. Hence

$$h = \frac{tc}{2} \tag{B.2}$$

(Note that, for both observers, the speed of the light is c; this is one of the fundamental postulates of relativity.)

Now we can relate t and t_0 by considering the geometry of the situation, shown in Fig B.1. In time t, the train travels a distance d given by

$$d = v \times t \tag{B.3}$$

By Pythagoras' theorem, we can see that h, d and l are related by

$$h^2 = \left(\frac{d}{2}\right)^2 + l^2 \tag{B.4}$$

Substituting equations (B.1), (B.2) and (B.3) into (B.4) gives

$$\frac{t^2 c^2}{4} = \frac{v^2 t^2}{4} + \frac{t_0^2 c^2}{4}$$

Simplifying and rearranging gives

$$t^2(c^2 - v^2) = t_0^2 c^2$$

and rearranging again gives

$$t^2 = t_0^2 \frac{c^2}{c^2 - v^2} = t_0^2 \frac{1}{1 - v^2/c^2}$$

Finally, taking the square root gives

$$t = \frac{t_0}{\sqrt{(1 - v^2/c^2)}}$$

v = velocity of carriage

path of light (as seen by A)

path of light (as seen by B) l h h

d

Fig B.1

B.2 RELATING ABSOLUTE AND APPARENT MAGNITUDES

Consider a star (or other astronomical object) of apparent magnitude m at a distance d from an observer on the Earth. Its absolute magnitude is M; i.e. if we could place it at a distance of 10 pc from the Earth, this would be its magnitude – see Fig B.2.

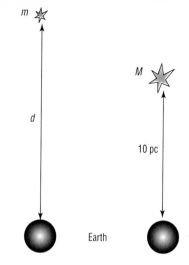

Fig B.2

It is awkward to work in magnitudes, since this scale is logarithmic; a change of 1 in magnitude represents a factor of 2.512 in brightness (see section 7.2). So we will first consider the intensity of light reaching an observer from the star. Suppose that the intensity of its light is i at distance d, and I when placed at 10 pc.

Now we know that if a star is twice as far away, its apparent brightness is reduced to a quarter, because of the inverse square law for the spreading out of light. The apparent brightness changes according to the inverse square of the ratio of distances. Hence we can write

$$\frac{I}{i} = \left(\frac{d}{10}\right)^2$$

Taking logs (to base 10) of both sides gives

$$\log I - \log i = 2 \log(d/10) \tag{B.5}$$

Now, from section 7.2, we have the following relationship between magnitude and intensity:

$$m = -2.512 \log i + \text{constant} \tag{B.6}$$

$$M = -2.512 \log I + \text{constant} \tag{B.7}$$

Subtracting (B.6) from (B.7), the constants cancel, and we have

$$M - m = -2.512(\log I - \log i)$$

Substituting in (B.5) gives

$$M - m = -2.512 \times 2 \log(d/10)$$

or

$$m - M = 5.024 \log(d/10)$$

B.3 DOPPLER SHIFT OF WAVELENGTH

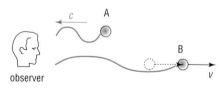

Fig B.3

When a star (or other astronomical object) is moving away from us, its light is red-shifted; there is a change in its wavelength.

Consider two stars, A and B, as shown in Fig B.3. Initially, they are side-by-side. Each emits a single wave of light in time t (a tiny fraction of a second).

Star A is stationary; its light has wavelength λ. Since the wave is travelling at speed c, its wavelength is

$$\lambda = ct \tag{B.8}$$

Star B is moving away. It emits a wave in the same time as A, but in this time star B moves a distance $v \times t$. So its wave is longer than the wave from A; it has been stretched, and its wavelength is λ', given by

$$\lambda' = ct + vt \tag{B.9}$$

Now the change in wavelength, $\Delta\lambda = \lambda' - \lambda$, is found by subtracting (B.8) from (B.9):

$$\Delta\lambda = vt \tag{B.10}$$

Finally, the fractional change in wavelength (the red-shift) is given by dividing (B.10) by (B.8):

$$\frac{\Delta\lambda}{\lambda} = \frac{vt}{ct} = \frac{v}{c}$$

The **red-shift**, $\Delta\lambda/\lambda$, is often denoted by the symbol z.

Appendix C

RESOURCES

C.1 USEFUL ADDRESSES

Professional organisations

British Astronomical Association (BAA), Burlington House, Piccadilly, London, W1V 9AG

Royal Astronomical Society (RAS), Burlington House, Piccadilly, London, W1V 0NL: aimed at the professional astronomer

Association for Astronomy Education (AAE), c/o Royal Astronomical Society, address as RAS above

Places to visit

London Planetarium, Marylebone Road, London, NW1 5LR (Tel: 0171 935 6861)

National Museum of Photography, Film and Television, Pictureville, Bradford, West Yorkshire, BD1 1NQ (Tel: 01274 727488)

National Maritime Museum and Old Royal Observatory, Greenwich, London, SE10 9NF (Tel: 0181 858 4422)

Jodrell Bank Science Centre, Lower Withington, Macclesfield, Cheshire, SK11 9DL (Tel: 01477 571339)

Royal Observatory, Blackford Hill, Edinburgh, EH9 3HJ (Tel: 0131 668 8100)

Armagh Planetarium, College Hill, Armagh, County Armagh, Northern Ireland, BT61 9DB (Tel: 01861 523689)

Science Museum, Exhibition Road, London, SW7 2DD (Tel: 0171 938 8000)

Providers of resources

British National Space Centre/Particle Physics and Astronomy Research Council, Educational Affairs, Polaris House, North Star Avenue, Swindon, Wiltshire, SN2 1ET (PPARC – Educational Affairs, Tel: 01793 442098; BNSC – Information Unit, Tel: 0171 215 0806/7/8): can provide schools with leaflets and booklets

National Aeronautics and Space Administration (NASA), Educational Division, Mail Code FE, Washington, DC 20546-00D1, USA

Many British universities have astronomy departments, which may be able to provide information and prospectuses for those wishing to study astronomy or astrophysics at degree level. Most professional astronomers study for a PhD before entering employment.

C.2 BOOKS AND OTHER SOURCES

Standard textbooks

Physics, by R. Hutchings. Thomas Nelson, 1990
Understanding Physics, by J. Breithaupt. Stanley Thornes, 1990
A-level Physics, by R. Muncaster. Stanley Thornes, 1993
Physics, by P. Fullick. Heinemann, 1995

Other textbooks

Relativity and Quantum Physics, by R. Muncaster. Stanley Thornes, 1995
Nuclear and Particle Physics, by D. Sang. Thomas Nelson, 1996

Specialist books: optics and photography

The Cambridge Astronomy Guide, by B. Liller and B. Mayer. Cambridge University Press, 1990

The Complete Photography Course, by M. Joseph and D. Saunders. Weidenfeld and Nicholson, 1995

Philip's Observer's Astrophotography – An Introduction, by H.J.P. Arnold. Philips, 1994

The Complete Kodak Book of Photography. Mitchell Beazley, 1994

Specialist books: relativity

Relativity for the Layman, by J.A. Coleman. Pelican, 1954

Mr Tompkins in Paperback, by George Gamow. Cambridge University Press, 1965 (reprinted 1993)

Einstein for Beginners, by J. Schwartz and M. McGuinness. Icon, 1992

Specialist books: astronomy and cosmology

Universe, by W. Kaufmann. Freeman, 1991

Foundations of Astronomy, by M. Seeds. Wadsworth, 1992

The Universe for Beginners, by F. Pirani and C. Roche. Icon, 1993

Newton for Beginners, by W. Rankin. Icon, 1993

Hawking for Beginners, by J.P. McEvoy and O. Zarate. Icon, 1995

The First Three Minutes, by S. Weinberg. Basic Books, 1977

Black Holes, by J.P. Luminet. Cambridge University Press, 1992

Astronomy and Optics, Teachers notes for guidance. Northern Examinations and Assessment Board, 1995

Norton's Star Atlas, 1978, and *Norton's 2000,* 1989. Hall and Inglis

A Brief History of Time, by S. Hawking. Bantam, 1988

Cosmology, by B. Milner. Cambridge University Press, 1995

Earth and Space, Teaching materials in support of science in the National Curriculum. Association for Science Education and AAE

Periodicals

Astronomy Now – available from newsagents or by subscription from Intra Press, Intra House, 193 Uxbridge Road, London, W12 9RA

Sky and Telescope – an American magazine, available by subscription from Sky Publishing Corporation, 49 Bay State Road, Cambridge, Mass 022838, USA

New Scientist – a weekly publication containing many up-to-date articles

Physics Review – an A-level review publication, Philip Allan publishers

Television programmes

The following may have features on areas covered in this book:

Horizon (BBC2)

Open University (BBC1 and BBC2)

Encyclopaedia Galactica (schools programme, Channel 4)

Equinox (Channel 4)

The Sky at Night (BBC1)

Various programmes on the Discovery Channel

C.3 ADVICE ON BUYING A TELESCOPE

Astronomical telescopes fall into two categories:

- Refracting telescopes – which use lenses
- Reflecting telescopes – which use mirrors

If you are interested in buying a telescope, a little caution is required. First of all, you will not see some of the spectacular images that appear in this and other books, although some very satisfying observations can be made. To buy a telescope that is capable of decent observations, you will probably need to spend a minimum of £400–£500. Therefore, the beginner would be well advised to seek advice and buy from a reputable source. Despite this, very keen amateurs have been known to construct their own reflecting telescopes. A stable mounting is required, as any vibrations in holding the telescope are magnified with the small field of view. The beginner is best advised to start with a decent pair of binoculars, such as 8 × 50. This means the angular magnification is 8× whilst the diameter of the objective lenses, which governs the light-gathering power, is 50 mm.

Refractors: False colour can be a major problem in cheaply made refracting telescopes. Generally, a telescope with an objective lens of diameter less than 60 mm is of limited use.

Reflectors: For the same magnifying power, reflecting telescopes are cheaper than refracting ones. Despite the sturdiness of alignment not being as good as with a refractor, a reflector is probably the better buy for a beginner. Objective mirrors greater than 100 mm in diameter are recommended.

If possible, the prospective buyer is advised to try out different telescopes before buying one, so as to gain some idea of the capabilities of a system and its likely cost.

Appendix D

ANSWERS TO QUESTIONS

Chapter 1

1.1 41 700 km; 6631 km
1.2 Difference = 3.97%
1.3 Ptolemaic system was geocentric, with epicycles, and Sun in third orbit from Earth. Also, stars all close together.
1.4 Distances involving Sun were very inaccurate, because no reliable method for determining this.
1.5 Orbits of inferior planets are inside Earth's orbit, so we are always looking towards the Sun when we see them.
1.6 As planet travelled along orbit to left, it might be moving along epicycle to right. This broke the notion that the heavens were perfect.
1.7 Close to Sun: planet is moving fastest, with max KE and least GPE; total energy is constant.
1.8, 1.9, 1.10 The gradient of the straight-line graph gives $k = 1.0 \, \text{y}^2 \, \text{AU}^{-3}$.
1.11 When Venus is on the opposite side of the Sun, it appears small but fully illuminated when viewed from the Earth.
1.12 m, km, AU, ly, pc
1.13 4.0×10^{16} m; 1.3 pc

Chapter 2

2.1 Newton's first law of motion.
2.2 6.67×10^{-9} N; very small
2.3 Weight = 586 N
2.4 2.1×10^{20} N
2.5 Newton's third law of motion; m_1 and m_2 are interchangeable.
2.6 2.66×10^{-6} rad s^{-1}
2.7 2.72×10^{-3} m s^{-2}
2.8 9.81 m s^{-2}
2.9 3600
2.10 3630
2.11 Yes!
2.12 $g = 1.63$ m s^{-2} on Moon, one-sixth of value on Earth.
2.13 2.0×10^{30} kg
2.14 Calculate (ratio of masses)/(ratio of radii squared).

Chapter 3

3.2 36 s
3.3 Geocentric models unlikely.
3.4 **(a)** 4×10^8 m s^{-1} **(b)** 3×10^8 m s^{-1}
3.5 **(a)** 4 m s^{-1} **(b)** 8 m s^{-1}
3.6 **(c)** $\gamma = 1$
3.7 Graph grows increasingly steeply.
3.8 **(a)** 10.75 y   **(b)** 6.45 y
3.9 $\gamma = 15$, $v = 0.997\,77c$
3.10 $\gamma = 1.67$
3.11 Graph decreases towards zero.
3.12 **(a)** 70.0 kg   **(b)** 70.000 04 kg
   (c) 70.35 kg
   (d) 80.8 kg   **(e)** 496.2 kg
   (f) ∞
3.13 **(a)** Mass returns to normal.
   (b) More energy needed to reach 5 m s^{-1}.
3.14 9×10^{15} J; 95 000
3.15 2.0×10^{-11} J

Chapter 4

4.1 Faster film; longer exposure time; wider aperture; focus on infinity; use a tripod.
4.3 Short and long exposure times.
4.4 Eye: 1%; film: 4%; CCD: 70%
4.5 Similar to grain size of slow film.
4.6 60, 100, 300; 6400 times brighter
4.7 **(a)** 60 cm   **(b)** 5
4.9 78.6°

Chapter 5

5.1 **(a)** 9.1×10^{-3} rad; 0.52° **(b)** 3.8×10^5 km
5.2 $3 \times 10^{-4} \times 360 \times 60/2\pi = 1.03$ arcmin
5.3 Telescope limited by atmosphere; eye limited by size of pupil.
5.4 **(a)** 9.1×10^{-5} rad   **(b)** 5×10^{-5} rad
5.5 Optical: 300 nm–20 μm approx.; radio: 1 cm–20 m approx.
5.6 No effect of atmosphere.
5.7 Light for photosynthesis, etc.
5.9 **(a)** 0.05 rad   **(b)** 1.2×10^{-5} m
5.10 Approx. 20 cm
5.11 2×10^{-4} rad
5.12 0.02 rad
5.13 0.013 rad
5.14 $\lambda \gg$ mesh size, so reflected.

Chapter 6

6.1 (a) Greater area   (b) No visible radiation

6.3 4000 K, 10 000 K, 6000 K (approx.)

6.4 16 times

6.5 7.7 times

6.6 (a) 4.5×10^{26} W   (b) 480 nm

6.7 209 W

6.8 (a) 7.5×10^{26} W   (b) 4.5×10^{18} m^2
      (c) 1.67×10^8 W m^{-2} (d) 7400 K

6.9 (a) Line   (b) Continuous

6.13 Sun, G; Sirius, A; Aldebaran, K; Betelgeuse, M

Chapter 7

7.1 (a) Sirius   (b) Arcturus
      (c) 2.7 pc, 8.8 ly, 5.57×10^5 AU

7.2 0.76 arcsec

7.3 (a) 4.8   (b) 6.1   (c) 27.5

7.4 Sirius

7.5 (a) 2.5 Mpc   (b) 250 pc (approx.)

7.7 1.3×10^7 m s^{-1}

7.8 (a) 4.5×10^7 m s^{-1} (b) 450 Mpc
      (c) 900 Mpc

7.9 20 000 million years; 10 000 million years

7.10 Radius

7.11 (a) Broader   (b) Red-shifted

7.12 (a) 3.0×10^{-7} rad s^{-1}; 1.81 m s^{-1}
      (b) 6.0×10^{-9} m

7.14 (a) Smaller   (b) A

Chapter 8

8.2 Betelgeuse: red supergiant; Aldebaran: red giant; Regulus: main sequence (white/blue); Rigel: white supergiant; Sirius B: white dwarf; Sun: main sequence.

8.5 Mass of hydrogen fused = 1.5×10^{29} kg; mass converted to energy = 9.86×10^{26} kg; lifetime = 2.3×10^{17} s = 7.3×10^9 years

8.6 Higher

8.7 10^9 years

Chapter 9

9.2 White dwarf: 3.6×10^8 kg m^{-3}; Earth: 5500 kg m^{-3}; Sun: 1400 kg m^{-3}

9.5 (a) 30 km
      (b) 1.8×10^{17} kg m^{-3}

9.6 No

9.7 Yes

Chapter 10

10.1 About 3.7 m

10.2 0.1–0.3 pc

10.5 Gravity

10.6 (a) 1200 km s^{-1} (b) 15 000 km s^{-1}
      (c) 22 000 km s^{-1} (d) 39 000 km s^{-1}
      (e) 61 000 km s^{-1}

10.7 (a) 79 Mly   (b) 976 Mly
      (c) 1450 Mly   (d) 2540 Mly
      (e) 3980 Mly

Chapter 11

11.4 10 000 million years

11.5 1.06 mm

11.8 (a) 0.5×10^{-26} kg m^{-3}
      (b) 3–11 H atoms

Index

Page references in **bold** refer to a table or an illustration.